MY LIFE FOR BEAUTY—THE FASCINATING AUTO-BIOGRAPHY OF HELENA RUBINSTEIN—IS ALSO "A COMPLETE MANUAL OF BEAUTY CARE FOR WOMEN OF ALL AGES."

—*Florida Times Union*

"The 'For Beauty' section of Mme. Rubinstein's book deals with formulas for beauty. She goes into detail on skin and hair care, makeup, diets, the use of perfumes and toiletries. She also offers advice on exercise. These are not . . . commercials for Helena Rubinstein products. They are sound and sensible words of wisdom."

—*Louisville Times*

"In the beauty advice section . . . she tells her readers how to hold their own 'day of beauty' at home. . . . You can almost hear her saying then, 'There are no ugly women—only lazy ones.' "

—*The New York Times Book Review*

"Fascinating . . . I particularly value the more than 20 pages of diets, including special meals for sleeping soundly, and an outline for setting up your own home beauty salon. . . ."

—*Philadelphia Inquirer*

HELENA RUBINSTEIN

MY LIFE
FOR
BEAUTY

PAPERBACK LIBRARY
A KINNEY SERVICE COMPANY
NEW YORK

PAPERBACK LIBRARY EDITION
First Printing: January, 1972

Library of Congress Catalog Card Number: 65-26675

This Paperback Library Edition is published by arrangement
with Simon and Schuster, Inc.

Paperback Library is a division of Coronet Communications, Inc.
Its trademark, consisting of the words "Paperback Library"
accompanied by an open book, is registered in the United States
Patent Office. *Coronet Communications, Inc., 315 Park Avenue
South, New York, N.Y. 10010.*

Contents

Introduction   9

Part One
MY LIFE

1 The Beginnings   13
2 Another Continent, Another Life   23
3 London   35
4 Paris—New York   51
5 Marriage Versus Business   63
6 Years of Change   73
7 Beautiful Things   87
8 Life Goes On   99

Part Two
FOR BEAUTY

1 Beauty Is Your Destination   113
2 Beauty Begins with Your Skin   155

3   What a Beauty Salon Can Mean to You   173

4   Eat Your Way to Beauty   181

5   Delightful New Ways to Exercise   205

6   A Hundred Faces for One   213

7   How to Manage Your Hair—and Glorify It   231

8   Hands, Fingers, and Nails ... Toes and Toenails   243

9   Fresh ... Fragrant ... and Ready for Anything   253

10   Beauty Potpourri   263

MY LIFE FOR BEAUTY

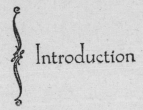 Introduction

The publication of this book coincides with the first anniversary of my mother's death on April 1, 1965. All her life, Mother wanted to share her knowledge of beauty with as many women as possible. She often said, "It's not enough for people to buy beauty products. They must be educated in how to use them." Madame Rubinstein traveled to every country in the world, and wherever she went she was genuinely interested in solving the problems of the women she met. Finally, in the later years of her long and productive life, she found time to gather together all the advice she was so anxious to give.

The story of her life was secondary to her. She never talked about herself unless questioned by a friend or reporter. It was really her friends and associates who urged her to make her fascinating life a part of history. Actually, her life and her work were so inseparable that a book dealing with one aspect without the other would seem incomplete.

Helena Rubinstein did live her life for beauty—not only beauty in the cosmetic sense, but in her love of beauty in the arts which she so actively encouraged and supported. I am glad that the readers of this book will be able to share the many facets of my mother's rich and full life. My Life for Beauty is dedicated to all of them.

—ROY TITUS

April 1, 1966

9

Part One

MY LIFE

1 $\{$ The Beginnings

I HAVE always felt that a woman has the right to treat the subject of her age with ambiguity until, perhaps, she passes into the realm beyond ninety. Then it is better that she be candid with herself and with the world.

I am well over the mark actually, ninety-four, but that does not mean that my spirit and my stubbornness have left me. The three armed bandits who broke into my New York home one morning recently must have expected to find a frail nonagenarian who would be so panicked by the sight of a gun, and by their threats, that they could walk off with a fortune in jewels. They had bound and gagged three of my employees, my butler, my maid, and a secretary, but I angrily insisted that they would get nothing from me and that taking my life would do them no good at all! They looked at one another, not knowing quite what to make of it, or of me—and decided they might as well leave.

A few days later I realized my foolhardiness and quaked for a few hours. But while it was happening I was strangely unafraid. I thought perhaps this was the way I was to make my exit from the world. Always a fatalist,

I said to myself, "I've had a good life, and I am not going to be pushed around at this late date."

My whole life has been a lucky one. Admittedly, I have had my ups and downs and my share of personal unhappiness. But in general fate has been kind—perhaps kindest of all in these later years by sustaining my zest and my interest in living.

Now in my tenth decade, I still thank God for many blessings. For the strength that propels me to the office each morning. For eyes clear enough to see without glasses, except for the reading which is now such a constant source of pleasure. For the stimulation of the bridge table, of good talk with many guests in my home, and for such amusements as the theater and the cinema which I love.

Chiefly I cherish the devotion of a large family and the many friends made and kept along the way. As for my business, it is still a major part of my life. I created it, I built it—and I hopefully plan that it will continue its success long after its originator has gone. The sales figures are as personal to me as a well-run household budget might be to other women, and I take pride in the fact that sales are increasing every year. The Helena Rubinstein staff of over thirty thousand in salons, factories, and laboratories scattered throughout the world I consider "my second family." I admit to a poor memory for names, but I know their faces well and take a personal interest in their lives and in the development of their careers. In fact, it has become very nearly a "family joke" in my offices that when I go on my tours of inspection and see again a familiar face I greet the face (though I may not remember its name!) with: "Are you happy? Are you learning? Are you growing stronger?"

"Work is your best beauty treatment," a friend said recently, laying on the flattering unction that I do not look my age. How would she know, I wondered. Few of my contemporaries are still about, to make comparisons with, but I am grateful for the flattery. It helps to keep my spirit young, and I am, after all, a woman. My face is still relatively unlined, and my hair in its perennial chignon is still midnight black. The hair, I admit, is aided by

14

Helena Rubinstein color out of a bottle. The skin owes its condition to heredity and a lifetime of care.

But work has indeed been my best beauty treatment. I believe in hard work. It keeps the wrinkles out of the mind and the spirit. It helps to keep a woman young. It certainly keeps a woman alive! Coming as I did from a conservative European background, my attitude as an individualist—a girl who preferred to make it on her own rather than stay at home— was all the more unusual.

I was born in 1870, in Cracow, Poland, on Christmas Day, the first child of Augusta and Horace Rubinstein. Before I was half-grown, I found myself the eldest of eight sisters. Our only brother died in infancy.

Cracow was, and still is, a medieval, feudal-looking town, an intellectual and cultural center. Here we were all brought up. We lived in a large old house near Rynek Square, close to the university. It was a house filled to overflowing with the overstuffed furniture of the nineteenth century and the varied collections of a father who had a passion for papers and books. Oil lamps were used to light the rooms, and in winter we kept warm by the towering porcelain stoves which burned night and day.

My father was a strict, thoughtful man from a well-to-do family. When his own children began to arrive in rapid succession, he became a wholesale food broker, buying eggs from the local peasants and reselling them in quantity. He was not a very good businessman, and I remember recognizing this at an early age and trying to figure out ways to help him. Mama was one of those fortunate women who, despite a child every year and the pressure of mounting economic problems, managed to grow more beautiful with each passing year. Her figure was slim and magnificent. I can see her even now, with her straight back, her tiny feet, and wonderfully capable hands, wearing a simple black dress with a white lace collar at the neck.

Mama's appearance was important to her. She had a neighbor come in and help her with her hair, and I would sit on a stool at her feet and beg her to allow me to have my hair done too. Occasionally she would give way, and I learned the delight of having my own hair washed and then combed by hands that were deft and knowledgeable —my first salon experience.

My mother imbued her daughters with the philosophy of the times.

"Women influence the world through love," she would tell us. "Outer charm and inner beauty will give you the power to control your own lives and hold the love of the man you will marry."

We would gather in the living room near the glowing stove. My mother would surround herself with her eight daughters: Helena, Pauline, Rosa, Regina, Stella, Ceska, Manka, and Erna. Then in turn she would brush each head of hair, a hundred strokes, while we counted in chorus. We all had the same black, glossy, luxuriant locks, of which Mama was very proud.

Just how much beauty is God-given and how much is developed through a desire for it no one can say. But I do know that my mother's beauty lessons, basic as they were, disciplined me in the daily ritual of beauty care which was later to become the A, B, C of my own life-long philosophy. It was she who gave me the sense of confidence and self-fulfillment which can come from taking regular care of one's physical assets.

And then, the finger of fate . . . my mother's beauty cream.

A visiting actress friend, Modjeska, first introduced it to my mother. The cream was made for her by a Hungarian chemist, Dr. Jacob Lykusky, then living in Cracow. It was compounded, Modjeska said, from a mixture of herbs and essence of almonds, plus extracts from the bark of an evergreen tree. My mother was fascinated, insisted on meeting Dr. Lykusky, and from then on the Rubinstein household had a regular supply of the cream. In spite of the fact that she was quite old-fashioned, Mama encouraged all her daughters to use it. She would visit each of her daughters at bedtime, and if we had been out in the wind or snow during the day, she would gently fingerprint a little of the cream on our cheeks.

"It will make you beautiful," she would whisper, kissing us good night. "And to be beautiful is to be a woman."

It was, as I look back, an intensely feminine household, filled with gaiety, warmth, vanity, and tantrums. As the oldest, I was learning, even at twelve, to take responsibility. My sisters called me "The Eagle" because I ruled the nursery, high up under the eaves of the old house, with complete authority. I also served as interpreter and intercessor between the younger ones and our parents—excellent training for employee relations in later years. My mother, hard-pressed by her brood, relied on me. She put me in charge of the family linen, with full responsibility for keeping it clean and mended.

Although I had my chores and studies, I had many pleasures too. I remember we often visited with my grandparents in the suburbs, all ten of us, and the gardener, Stass, would make us miniature furniture with which we played. That, and my collection of tiny dolls, their faces carefully painted, undoubtedly started my passion for miniatures and for collecting.

I kept the dolls and treasured them for many years. During the enemy occupation of France during World War II, many were lost or stolen from my Paris apartment and from my country home in Combs-la-Ville. But I still have a collection of twenty thousand pieces of antique miniature furniture, started in nursery days in Cracow, and added to during fifty years of shopping and collecting throughout Europe. They are housed in seventeen miniature rooms, which form small recesses in the walls of one special room in my New York apartment. Each tiny arrangement is an authentic period piece, dating from the seventeenth century up to the present day; they are all dramatically lit and enclosed behind glass windows. One of them is a replica of Modigliani's Paris studio as I knew it after World War I. With such delicate objects as clocks, candelabra, and sets of dishes, most of them no bigger than shoe buttons and all faithfully accurate reproductions of their periods, these rooms constitute an authentic record of the cabinetmaker's art. Connoisseurs and art critics have traveled from many lands to see these miniature rooms, but I think I enjoy showing them to children most of all. And especially to my last-born grandchild, my son Roy's daughter, Helena, who is just six and the apple of my eye.

Life in the Cracow Rubinstein household was quite different from family life today, in which teen-agers exert so much influence over their world. My mother taught us all to knit and sew, and I was a great embroiderer. I could stitch a complex tablecloth in just a few days, and my skill must have been irritating to some of my contemporaries, for I have a hazy memory of one of my schoolmates cutting up my needlework out of sheer spite. As children of a large family we were loved, but we were not spoiled. And it never occurred to any of us to question our parents' judgment or to answer back.

I remember that a dancing master lived next door to us, and he often gave dancing parties—with boys. Most of the other local girls attended, and one afternoon I decided to join them. In the midst of the party I was terribly embarrassed to have my father arrive, in high dudgeon, and remove me from the premises. I don't know whether it was because I was his eldest daughter, or perhaps the most impetuous, but he was over-protective of me to a fault. On the other hand, because he had no son, he would talk over his plans and projects with me, and since I was good at figures, he depended on me to help him with his bookkeeping. Once, when I was nearly fifteen, he was taken ill before an important business meeting. It was too late to cancel the meeting, which was to take place in a neighboring town, and of course there was no such thing as a telephone in those days. I offered to go in his place, and after much talk and family consultation I was allowed to go and speak for my father. Before I left the house Mama whispered in my ear, "If you want to be really clever, listen well and talk little."

The fact that I was able to bring off a very good deal was, I think, largely due to my youth and inexperience (and Mama's advice), which must have dumfounded the others at the meeting. But my sense of triumph was a foretaste of what business achievement could mean.

On another occasion a wagonload of eggs, ordered by my father, was delayed at the city gates because of a four-day religious holiday. The family counted heavily on the sale of the eggs, and if the authorities were to impound them in the summer heat, they most certainly would have gone bad. Taking matters into my own hands, I went off to see the city officials myself. With wiles, pleadings and

18

tears, I told them of the family difficulties. That same afternoon the eggs were released.

Sometimes taking things into my own hands had disastrous results. When I was about fifteen, I developed a hatred for the heavy, old-fashioned furniture in my room at home. One morning, when both my parents were away on a short holiday, I woke up with the brilliant idea of selling all the furniture in my room and using the proceeds for new, "modern" furnishings. I had no idea of the affection my father had for the pieces that, to me, were just old dust traps. Calling in a secondhand dealer, I disposed of the lot. Then I hurried to the shops and bought lots of shiny, new furniture. Delighted with the result, I felt sure that my father would be too. Never will I forget the look on his face when he saw the room! He was almost too shocked for anger, but it was obvious that he was heartbroken. He went straight to the secondhand dealer and bought everything back! He would be pleased, I think, to know that the incident impressed me so strongly; to this day I have never got rid of anything without long thought and expert advice.

When my days at the gymnasium were ended, Father was eager for me to study medical science.

Although I was a serious student even then, it surprised me that my father should elect such a career for one of his daughters. Women in medical schools and hospitals were a rarity, and they were not exactly welcomed by the medical world, which was still considered to be exclusively masculine. I wish I could say that the time spent at my medical studies was a success. It was not. Although I thoroughly enjoyed the laboratory work, I grew dizzy at the first whiff of antiseptic and fainted at the sights and odors of the sickroom. No matter how I tried to be attentive and studious, it was impossible for me to overcome my own weaknesses. My sleep was haunted by fear of dismissal from the university, a fear which I did not dare disclose to my parents. It was my mother who noticed how thin and unhappy I had become, and she guessed the reason why.

"Then Helena must get married," Father said.

With the strange practicality which ran through his unbusinesslike personality he began to look around and picked a wealthy widower of thirty-five as the perfect husband for me. I was fond enough of him, but I was eighteen and romantic, and I would not accept him as a husband. Rebellious, I persuaded myself that I had fallen in love with a handsome young medical student at the university. His name was Stanislaw, and I remember he had blue-black hair and strikingly blue eyes. When he proposed in the strictly formal manner of the day, asking Father for my hand, Father was furious! There were shouts and tears and tantrums. It was all too much for me. I felt thwarted; my life was in ruins; I was obviously going to be an old maid. There was nothing left for me in Poland.

That was when I decided to write to my mother's brother in Australia, Uncle Louis. He had emigrated to Australia after his wife, a lovely Polish girl, had died giving birth to a daughter. The child, Eva, had been left with us until her teens, and since she was almost as old as I, we had become quite close. When she rejoined her father in Australia we maintained a correspondence, and from her letters, life in that part of the world sounded much more promising than in Cracow. I convinced myself that I longed to see my cousin again, and I told my father I was writing to my uncle. Still angry with me (I realize now how hurt he must have been), he agreed and wrote to Uncle Louis that if he wanted me he could keep me as long as he liked.

Uncle Louis wrote back cordially. I was so excited by his welcoming words that I ignored the warning in his letter: "Life is very different here, and the climate is hot." A different life was exactly what I wanted. And if it was hot, I would have a chance to wear all my white pleated dresses and leghorn hats and to use my parasols. (I was always somewhat of a fashion plate and loved to have pretty clothes, most of which were run up at home.) I was young, and with all the hubbub about my two suitors, perhaps my head was turned a bit? But more than anything, I wanted to break with the past and find my own identity.

Heartlessly I counted the days until my departure, ignoring my mother's tears and the fact that I was putting half a world between my sisters and myself. In years to come I would learn of the heartache of refugees from racial or religious persecution and from political oppression. (Although my family is Jewish, we were fortunate, through location and circumstances, never to have suffered this cruelty.) But mine was a different kind of flight—from a narrow, circumscribed world to the unknown and the challenging.

Gaily I set out to make the long trip to Australia by myself—without fully realizing that I would be going so far away. If now and then a few doubts entered my mind, I was determined to keep them from my family. As the date of my departure neared I packed my old-fashioned trunk with all my possessions, including twelve pots of my mother's beauty cream. Through it all the excitement mounted, and when it came time to kiss my parents and my sisters goodbye, although there were tears, my head was so filled with wonder and anticipation that I felt as if my feet were barely touching the ground.

2 Another Continent, Another Life

TRAVELING when I was young was different from jet travel today, when I can weekend in Paris and London and be back to work in New York on Monday. First there was the seemingly endless railroad journey from Cracow to Hamburg. From the port of Hamburg I sailed through the Mediterranean, crossed the Suez Canal, and then steamed slowly across the Indian Ocean to Melbourne. Then came the long journey by coach over the dusty inland road to Coleraine, where I found a small settlement of some two thousand people living very simply in a township which derived its name from the Gaelic, meaning "land covered with ferns." I never saw any ferns there—only hundreds and hundreds of bleating sheep and bony cattle.

Altogether the journey from Cracow took three months. The sea voyage was the best part of it. The ship was small compared to modern liners, but the passengers were friendly and I had a wonderful time. I have always been very shy socially, and for a girl of eighteen, even a shy girl, that trip could not have been more satisfactory, for there were three unattached, elegant young men fighting for their turn to dance with me each evening. One was an Englishman, the other two Italians—and I could speak not a word of either language at the time! Like many young girls, I was flirtatious in spite of my shyness, and surely vain; but I had been brought up with rigid, inflexible ideals of morality quite different from today's casual attitudes. Even kissing seemed to me immoral, and the mysteries of sex were still mysteries. There is no question that this prevented me from forming interesting alliances, but on the other hand, it left my life uncluttered, free for other pursuits. To some it may seem curious that I, with my strict upbringing and almost puritanical training, should have devoted my lifetime to building a business based largely on women's desire to be attractive to men. And yet, though I have loved, and loved deeply, I have always admired beauty for its own sake—rather than for its seductive qualities.

Somerset Maugham once said it differently. "Beauty," he wrote, "is a grave word. It is a word of high import. It is used lightly now . . . of the weather, of a garden, of a syllogism; 'beautiful' serves as a synonym for good or pretty or pleasing or nice or engaging or interesting. But beauty is none of these. It is much more. It is a force. It is an enravishment. It is not a figure of speech when people say it takes their breath away; in certain cases it may give you the same suffocating shock as when you dive into ice-water. The impact of beauty is to make you feel greater than you are, so that for a moment you seem to walk on air; and the exhilaration and release are such that nothing in the world matters any more. You are wrenched out of yourself into a world of pure spirit. It is like falling in love. It *is* falling in love."

If that is so, then I fell in love with beauty a long, long time ago, but what I wanted was to create beauty—not to be blinded by it.

During the long sea journey I forgot all about my heartaches; I even forgot to be homesick. But on my first day at Coleraine I was overcome with loneliness. The sun was strong, the wind violent. The never-ending sweep of pasture, broken here and there by a blue gum tree, presented a very different picture from the one I had imagined. Tears came into my eyes when I thought of my family,

24

of my home and the lovely city of Cracow, with its green parks and wonderful chestnut trees on the banks of the river Vistula, and the highlands stretching up to the Carpathians.

To the hard-working, kindly Australians, the little girl from Poland must have looked like someone from another world. Anxious to make a good impression on my relatives, I had taken great care over my appearance, and I arrived wearing one of my most elegant white pleated dresses, with a large straw hat and, of course, wearing high-heeled button shoes. I also carried a parasol, but I found it quite impossible to keep the dust out of my eyes and at the same time hold the parasol over my head in the correct European manner.

My uncle's neighbors, who had ridden in from their stations beyond Koroite Creek to welcome me, politely admired my inappropriate clothes, but they must have laughed among themselves at my naïve vanity.

It took several months to accustom myself to the many changes which life in Australia made necessary, and it was not easy to hide my chagrin at realizing that there were many sacrifices involved in being an individualist. However, my cousins could not have been kinder. But I refused to store away my modish European clothes. Stubbornly I dressed up for every possible occasion, and I even defied Eva's sound advice by continuing to wear my impractical high-heeled shoes on a terrain that had never been intended for anything so frivolous.

My new friends could not get over the milky texture of my skin. It was, in fact, no better than the average girl's in my home town in Poland, but to the ladies of Victoria, with their sun-scorched, wind-burned cheeks, its city-bred alabaster quality seemed remarkable.

The twelve pots of face cream with which my mother had sent me off, with instructions never, never to neglect my complexion, were to be the cornerstone of my life. When the women in Coleraine heard about this cream they all wanted to try it, and soon nearly all the cream in the twelve jars I had brought with me had been given to friends, with their friends clamoring for more. I wrote to Mama asking for an additional supply. She began to send replacements every month, and as soon as the cream arrived I would store in it the cellar of my uncle's house to keep it at the right temperature.

Even so, the demand was exceeding the supply. It worried me that I had to disappoint so many who had been so good to me on my arrival in their country. I longed to be able to help them all. It was this experience, I believe, which first made me aware of other women's beauty problems. I wanted to help them to protect the beauty of their skins and their natural good looks.

I might have settled down with a small successful home business in the outback of Australia if the atmosphere had not subtly changed. Nothing I did seemed to please my Uncle Louis any more. A distant cousin of mine asked me to marry him, but I could not imagine myself as a rancher's wife. The face of Stanislaw, with whom I still corresponded, had become little more than a vague memory. Often I went to bed crying, longing for my mother, but I knew I could never go back to the quiet, uneventful life of Cracow, even though I was homesick and miserable. I had made another mistake. I would have to leave Coleraine—but where was I to go? I was a stranger in a strange country, speaking little English and still very young. At last came an inspiration. I knew that in my mother's skin cream I had something to sell that others wanted to buy. I would open a shop, although I wasn't very clear as to what sort of shop it would be. But first I had to get to Melbourne, to a metropolis, where I felt there would be more scope for my ideas and energies. Once more against the wishes of my elders, I took things into my own hands.

I had a good friend in Melbourne, a young Englishwoman I had met on the boat coming over to Australia, who was the wife of the Governor's A.D.C. We had corresponded, and when I wrote to her of my plan she invited me to stay with her.

I felt a little diffident about accepting her hospitality, but instead of refusing her invitation, I suggested that perhaps she might allow me to teach her two young children German while I was her guest. She was delighted with the idea, and soon afterward I left my uncle's ranch for Melbourne.

Here I was given my first introduction to "society." There were receptions and parties almost every day, and with my host and hostess I was invited to many places. It was all very exciting for a time and I reveled in it. But in my heart I knew this could only be a temporary respite. Somehow I had to make a success of my life in my own way. Over and over again I pondered on the possibilities of the family beauty cream, until I saw clearly what I had to do. I would open up a shop, but it would be more than just a shop where my cream would be sold; I would *teach* Australian women how to protect their skins against the hot, dry climate and the strong sun. In Europe, in those days, beauty arts were practiced discreetly behind closed doors, generally in someone's home, but in Australia no such services were available. I would bring to the Australian women the arts of beauty through the medium of my cream and my shop—my beauty salon! I was tremendously excited. The idea was born; the cream was a reality—now all I needed was the capital with which to start.

Indeed, my lucky star must have been in its ascendancy. Upon arriving in Melbourne, I sought out another of the friends I had made on board ship, Miss Helen MacDonald. I told her of my plan, and she constantly encouraged me, saying over and over, "You must believe in yourself as I believe in you." She did more than that. She was far from wealthy, but she insisted upon lending me her life savings, the two hundred and fifty pounds (then approximately $1,500) I would need to start my venture. It was the only sum of money I have ever borrowed, but I have never regretted it. It was repaid with interest before many months had passed.

With one half of the money I ordered a large stock of the cream in bulk, directly from Dr. Lykusky in Poland, purchased the necessary jars and labels locally, and hand-lettered them myself. The rest of the money I spent on the rent and furnishings of a good-sized second-floor room at 274 Collins Street, in the heart of Melbourne. The light was excellent, and immediately I saw the place, I knew it was exactly what I was looking for. I could divide it into three small rooms, paint the walls white, and furnish it with light, inexpensive pieces.

One room would be my "kitchen." Even to this day I think of our immense laboratories, of *all* scientific labora-

27

tories, as "kitchens." Once I startled the great Mme. Curie by asking her to let me see her "cuisine."

I painted the walls of my first salon myself. The curtains I made from the lovely white full-skirted dresses I had brought from Poland. Bamboo and rattan furniture was used in conservatories in Australia, and I knew that it was inexpensive. I filled the three small rooms with these comfortable chairs, painted them white to match the walls and curtains, and covered the seats in bright calico (like the covers we had in our home in Cracow). By the time I was ready to open my first salon, the three rooms looked as light and friendly and attractive as I could make them.

I even painted the signboard proclaiming my name to the world for the first time: HELENA RUBINSTEIN, BEAUTY SALON.

People streamed in, mostly out of curiosity at first, for a beauty salon was unheard of in those days. The majority stayed for advice, however, and few left without a jar of my hand-labeled cream.

Examining for the first time so many skins at close quarters and discussing with customers their different problems, I began to realize how much one skin differs from another. And it dawned on me that, wonderful as my cream undoubtedly was (and still is), it would not solve every irregularity and could itself be improved. I would have to learn how to adjust the formulation of the cream and to create new creams and lotions to suit different skin types. There was only one thing to do. At the end of the working day I would close up shop and spend long evenings experimenting in my "kitchen."

I began to classify skin types as oily, dry, combination, or normal; and I taught each of my customers the correct massage movements to use while applying the cream—depending upon the texture of her skin.

Then came my really lucky break. Sydney's foremost woman journalist had heard of Australia's first beauty salon and she came to Melbourne to interview me. She reported every word I said in her widely read columns, adding that in her own opinion my cream was the answer to every Australian woman's prayers. As a result of her articles, I was deluged with letters from every part of the country, all enclosing money orders. I was completely overwhelmed, for I had not nearly enough stock to fill the demand. I acknowledged every order by hand, sitting up several nights to do so, and I offered to return the money orders to those for whom I had no cream at the moment. Only one person asked for her money back!

With my new capital in hand, I wrote to Dr. Lykusky, the creator of my cream in Poland, asking him to come to Australia to work with me. To my delight he accepted, agreeing to stay for a short time. In fact, he remained many months, teaching me to formulate the original cream which we christened "Creme Valaze." (It has been a part of the Helena Rubinstein line ever since, and is today still a success, as "Wake-Up Cream.") We also formulated several related cleansing creams, astringent lotions, and a medicated soap, so as to have a complete treatment line.

I firmly believe that nothing that is worth while comes easily, and if I was lucky in not having to wait long for success, I more than made up for it by working eighteen hours out of every twenty-four. During this period, too, I lost many a beau and missed the fun of being lightheartedly young. Whenever a young man wanted to take me out on a Saturday, I would ask him to call for me at the salon. Then when he arrived I would sometimes be so absorbed in mixing a batch of cream that, without thinking, I would hand him a mixing paddle and set him to work too.

One friend had a beautiful clear handwriting, and I would beg him to spend the afternoon writing business letters for me; another, big and broad-shouldered, was made to shift furniture around and to carry the heavy vats of cream up from the storeroom to the first floor; a third, who was not as energetic, had to sit and paste labels on the parcels ready for posting. It was not surprising that soon I had no male friends at all, and there were no more invitations.

But the business was growing. I lived simply and saved every penny. In two years from the opening of the salon in Melbourne my bank balance changed from a debit of £250 (the sum I borrowed from Miss MacDonald) to a credit of £12,000. Soon I would have to find larger premises.

A new building, McEwan House, had just gone up at 243 Little Collins Street, and here I took a seven-room suite on the first floor. This time each room was painted in a slightly different shade of green instead of the dead white I had chosen for my first salon. I did this more as a reminder of home than anything else, for I was still homesick at times and would dream of the changing seasons; the green was to remind me of the lovely parks and gardens of Cracow where I played as a child with my sisters.

I knew it was no longer possible for me to manage alone, and I decided to write home, asking one of my sisters to join me. Fortunately my sister Ceska (the third youngest of our large family, who now directs the business throughout Great Britain) had studied chemistry in Berlin with the celebrated Dr. Joseph Kapp. She agreed to come to Australia—although she was only eighteen at the time. (Sending home for a sister or a relative was to become a habit with me. I did so repeatedly as time went on, and we are still essentially a family business.)

One stroke of luck which helped to popularize my new salon during those early years was the visit of a charming English actress, Nellie Steward. She was the star of a touring company which had just opened in Melbourne with phenomenal success, and her name was on everyone's lips.

The first time I saw Nellie Steward she rushed up the stairs to the salon and, almost before she was in the door, demanded the return of the "peaches-and-cream complexion" for which she had been so famous in England. She told me that since her arrival in Australia she had been riding about in an open carriage, with the sun beating down on her face. Her skin was dry and a mass of freckles by that time. "What can I do?" she exclaimed. "After all, people must *see* me!" I introduced her to my Creme Valaze which would protect her skin and keep it moisturized. I explained, too, that the success of Creme Valaze in Australia was due in part to a mild bleaching ingredient. Regular use of the cream would assure her the translucent complexion so fashionable at the time, and it would also help to remove her freckles.

In addition to the price of the cream, I received a grateful hug from Miss Steward. There was something about this impetuous young woman that I liked, and from that first meeting we became friends. Since I could rarely leave the salon in time to meet her before the evening performance, and it was necessary for me to be up and awake very early in the mornings, she took to dropping by now and then in the late afternoons, and occasionally she would bring along a friend.

One day she came by with Nellie Melba, the opera singer, who was making one of her many "farewell tours" in her native Australia. Statuesque and imposing in a jet-embroidered gown, with an enormous hat swathed in ostrich feathers, the great coloratura seemed to fill the whole place with her presence. Her self-assurance delighted me. In her magnificent voice Melba announced, "If you can give Miss Steward a peaches-and-cream complexion, you can surely give me one to match my voice . . . like this!" And she burst into an aria from *Aïda!*

I asked Miss Melba to be seated, so that I could examine her skin, but she insisted on standing. Since she completely dwarfed my four feet ten inches, the only thing for me to do was to pull up a chair and stand on it. This sent her off into peals of laughter.

Although I was still in my early twenties, my name was beginning to be known in Australia. I had already started training a small staff of beauticians. My hope was that after they had completed their apprenticeship they would be able to help me run salons in other Australian cities.

In spite of being busy for long hours every day, I never neglected the care of my skin. There was simply no time for a visit to a hairdresser, however. I washed my hair myself, dried it quickly, and found that the easiest thing (and the tidiest) was to comb it all back and pin it into a chignon. When eventually I went home to Cracow and my mother saw me for the first time in years, she did everything possible to persuade me to change it. "It is unattractively severe for a young girl, Helena," she said. Yet many years later Graham Sutherland, the English portrait painter, complimented me on the simple line of my hair style, which he said emphasized the strength of my head.

With my sister Ceska and our little team of assistants the business fell into an organized routine, although it took a while for Ceska to settle down in Australia. She was lonely and unhappy at first. But Ceska is quick and adaptable, and before long she took to her new life and her work with enthusiasm. She always has been tremendously interested in laboratory research. She spent many hours in my "kitchen" when she was not seeing a certain attractive young Englishman, Edward Cooper, who was known in the Australian racing world for his fine string of horses. I had a feeling that soon they would be married —as indeed they were.

The time came when the business could be efficiently run without my constant presence. The old demons began to goad me once more. I was eager to move on to bigger things, knowing even then that I had only just begun. Friends urged me to take time off. "You are young only once. Enjoy yourself!" They could not understand that I was happiest working, experimenting, creating. Already I was dreaming of seeing my name in all the capital cities of the world.

Yet my dreams were practical ones. I was determined to put an end forever to all the vague, poetic nonsense about elixirs of youth and magic potions. The only sure way to beauty, I was convinced, was the sound, scientific approach. But if I wanted to make my dreams a reality, there was a great deal more I had to learn.

I have always had a passion for detail. Although I trust my employees to carry out my instructions, I must first know how to do everything myself. I must be satisfied as to the absolute purity of each of my preparations and their ability to do all that I claim for them.

The one way to assure this was to visit the medical centers of Europe, become a student once again and learn everything I could about the human body and its needs. Vienna, Berlin, Paris, and then London! These magic names repeated themselves over and over again in my brain. They were the great centers of culture and learning. There I would be able to meet famous professors and scientists and talk with acknowledged experts.

But first I would pay a visit to my parents.

When I returned to Cracow, I found that it had not changed at all, yet to my eyes it appeared to have grown smaller. It was still a beautiful city, but I thought it quiet and dull. Nothing seemed to be happening there. I had by then seen something of the world and met many people.

Life in Cracow had become alien to me. It was no longer the place where I could live my life.

I am sorry to think now that I cut short my visit to my parents' home; but I had to hurry to Paris to begin my studies under the famous dermatologist, Dr. Berthelot. I worked in his laboratories all day, and at night, too, greedily reading everything I could lay my hands on regarding the scientific care of the skin. From him I learned the intricate anatomy of the skin and the principles which govern its appearance and health. From great surgeons I learned what could be accomplished by facial surgery (then in the very early stages of development). I learned, too, all I could about the body's metabolism and diet and their relation to health and beauty.

I spent months touring the fashionable clinics in Europe, to observe their methods. In Vienna I met a brilliant woman doctor, Frau Doktor Emmie List, who became a close personal friend and who joined me a few years later in London. Those were, I think, the most stimulating years of my life. I was learning, learning all the time. Everything was new and exciting.

When finally I went back to Australia, I was full of great plans for the future. The year spent in Europe had made me more than ever aware that the work I had chosen to fill my life was completely satisfying; I had neither time nor thought for anything else. I was growing up with my business and completely dedicated to it. Nothing was allowed to distract me from work. Or so I thought—until one day an American newspaperman, a friend of my sisters in Cracow, called at the salon to see me. His name was Edward William Titus. He was of Polish extraction; he had been everywhere, and he was a wonderful conversationalist. I was enthralled by him. Until then most of the people I had known had led rather narrow, humdrum lives; they were afraid of change and suspicious of new ideas. Edward Titus excited my imagination; he was an intellectual, interested in everything, and he had many friends in the literary and artistic world. New ideas held no fear for him.

He took me to the theater and to concerts. I enjoyed being with him. He opened a whole new world to me. Soon we were seeing a great deal of each other. Neverthe-

33

less, I was quite unprepared when one day he said, "Helena, I can see you are determined to build an empire. Marry me and we will do it together."

From the moment I had left Cracow, and Stanislaw, behind me, marriage had never entered into my scheme of things; but I strongly suspected that if I remained in Australia, sooner or later I would marry Edward Titus. During the course of a lifetime a woman meets many people, talks with them, laughs with them, makes friends with them. Then, suddenly, along comes a man she has never seen before, and from that moment he is the only one who counts. I was falling in love—something I had not bargained for. I knew I had to get away. Indeed, I was not ready for marriage, and it frightened me a little.

3 London

I DECIDED to go to London, then the world center of thought, taste, money, and beauty. From the other side of the globe it appeared the richest, the gayest, the most elegant capital in the world. This was the city in which I most wanted to succeed, and nothing could keep me from it. Yet I was torn both ways. I hesitated over leaving Edward, because I really cared deeply for him. It was the most difficult decision I had ever had to make, since it did not concern me alone. Either way I would not be happy. But in the end I knew that I would have to go. As soon as my decision was made, I booked passage for Southampton.

The truth is that my heart has always been divided—between the people I have loved and the ambition that would not let me rest. I know that for a time Edward felt quite crushed, but he promised he would follow me before very long. I asked only for time, for I wanted him as much as he wanted me. But first I had to establish my London salon.

Once again there were lonely months for me. I had no support from any of my friends in Australia. "Stay as you are, my girl, and you'll be a comfortable little millionairess in no time," they said. "Try to set up a beauty shop in London and they'll slaughter you." But I could not, would not, believe that English women, many of whom had been good friends to me in Australia, would prove so unapproachable on their own ground.

London was then at the height of its Edwardian splendor. In the great houses of Mayfair and Belgravia, at which I would gaze in admiration as I walked along the pavements, lived some of the most elegant and demanding women in the world. Theirs was a closely guarded, impregnable society, revolving around the urbane and dazzling King Edward VII and his beautiful Queen Alexandra. The great hostesses of the day, all enjoying royal favor in varying degrees, were Mrs. George Keppel, Mrs. Ronnie Greville, and Mrs. Willie James.

I felt myself very much a foreigner in this strange city where all doors seemed closed except to a select few. Accustomed to being busy, I was also a bit lost without my "kitchen" in which I might at least have kept myself occupied producing creams and lotions. I missed the stimulation and encouragement of Edward's company. Sometimes I wondered whether I had been wrong not to marry Edward when he asked me. But I kept reassuring myself that I had something every woman wanted—a skill based on the knowledge of how to create and develop beauty.

It was my own loneliness that gave me impetus. I had taken a small third-floor flat in Arlington Street, where I shared expenses with an Australian girl who had come to London at about the same time as I had. Early each morning I would set out to hunt for premises which would be suitable for my beauty salon. In this great city, however, there could be no question of upstairs rooms furnished with bamboo and rattan. If I wanted the "carriage trade," my salon would have to be in Mayfair.

Tired and more than a little despondent by lunchtime, I would go to a matinee in the afternoon to keep up my spirits, while I rested my feet; and often I would find myself in the theater again in the evening to fill the solitary hours. The London theater was tremendously exciting to me, and before long I had seen every play in town. There were wonderful, colorful personalities on the English stage

36

in those days—Ellen Terry, Mrs. Pat Campbell, Sir George Alexander, Sir Henry Irving. I saw the lovely Lily Elsie in *The Merry Widow* at Daly's at least five times, and I was a constant visitor to the Duke of York's Theatre while Isadora Duncan was dancing there. I was completely under the spell of her peculiar magnetism, marveling at how she managed to combine the grace of a jungle cat with the manners of a great lady.

It was some years later that I met Isadora Duncan at a supper party given by Margot Asquith. The great dancer walked into the room looking like the central character in a Greek tragedy. Draped around her head and shoulders she wore a chiffon scarf which trailed behind her as she moved. The effect was dramatic but not too practical. All during supper Isadora kept rearranging and adjusting her scarf. Shyly I asked her, "Wouldn't it be safer and just as lovely if it were shorter?" She was surprised at my temerity, but she was also amused. "My dear child," she replied, "what about the effect?" A few years afterward Isadora Duncan was dead, killed by her passion for long trailing scarves. She had been driving in her open Bugatti, with a scarf wound around her neck and the ends streaming in the wind. Somehow they became entangled in the spokes of the revolving wheels, and before the car stopped she had been strangled.

I remember Gaby Deslys, a figure of immense glamor and daring. In low-cut velvet gowns of her own design, she never failed to show as much of her bosom as was socially permissible. She made a point of displaying her lovely legs, too, in the sheerest of lace stockings, and she wore incredibly high heels studded with rhinestones. Even in death she was a legendary figure, for she died of a throat ailment which might have been cured by an operation—but to Gaby Deslys death itself was preferable to a scar.

These and other once famous people play a far larger part in my memory today, however, than they did in my life during those early years. In 1907 I knew no one in London, and as I walked from one street to another I had only one purpose in mind, to find the right premises for the salon I hoped to establish. There were moments when I knew discouragement, but they were few. Already I had learned the invaluable lesson that the greater the goal, the greater the price one must be prepared to pay; and when my body and nerves ached at the end of the day, I welcomed sleep, for the day to come would mean more miles of walking and searching. Sooner or later I felt certain that I would find what I was looking for.

When I heard, by chance, that the house of Lord Salisbury, one of England's great political figures of that era, was available for rent, I flew around to look at it. It was a handsome Georgian town house of four floors and twenty-six rooms, located in Grafton Street. The rent was several thousand pounds per annum, more than I could really afford, but I gambled on my luck. I took the house, and I was off on my newest project!

Contractors, painters, carpenters, all had to be hired and given instructions. When I think that the sum of my experience up to that time had been gleaned from my one Australian venture, where the problems had been so different from anything which London was to present, it amazes me that I should have embarked on the new London enterprise without questioning my own abilities or consulting with anyone—even to the interior décor of the salon there and of the entire building! I knew little of what made for really smart interior decorating. When had there been time for me to learn? Yet I had no hesitation as to what I wanted. Instinct and determination carried me along. I remained in London only as long as was necessary to get the work under way to my satisfaction. Then I left for Paris and Vienna, partly to fill in the tedious weeks of waiting until I could open my doors to the public, partly to engage a glamorous, capable staff—but chiefly to assure myself that I knew everything there was to know about the latest developments in beauty and skin care. I managed, too, to persuade my doctor friend in Vienna, Emmie List, to join my staff in London. Busy as I was with a hundred other things, I even made time to formulate a number of new preparations. It was as if I had forgotten the meaning of fatigue, and when I returned to London again I was fresh and eager and full of new ideas.

Walking up Grafton Street on my way to the emerging salon one day, I saw a familiar figure standing outside my new premises, gazing up at the temporary sign with my name on it. It was Edward Titus. True to his promise, he had followed me from Australia. Characteristically his first words were not at all what I expected. "Very nice, those white brocade curtains, Helena," he said. "But if you really want to set London talking you'll have to do better. Come with me to the Ballet Russe this evening, and I'll show you what's really new."

Sergei Diaghilev's Ballet Russe was then on its first visit to England. It was also my first visit to the ballet anywhere. I was entranced by Nijinsky, but what thrilled me as much as the dancing were the décors of Léon Bakst and Alexandre Benois. Accustomed as I was to the sweet-pea pastel stage sets of the times, the electric combinations of purple and magenta, orange and yellow, black and gold, excited me beyond measure! Warm, passionate colors, they were as far removed from my virginal whites and noncommittal greens as anything could be. Edward was right. After the ballet, late as it was, I went straight back to the salon and tore down my white brocade curtains. Next day I gave orders for them to be replaced with the brilliant color schemes I had fallen in love with the night before, and over the years they have been seen in Rubinstein salons everywhere.

I began to see Edward daily. He was the first man I had ever known who could make me forget business, and during the weeks that followed he captivated me by the sheer force of his personality. In many ways we were direct opposites. I was shy, and still am. I prefer to listen rather than talk. I live very much within myself and am completely confident and relaxed only in business. Edward was an extrovert, a man ahead of his time, forward-thinking, curious and impulsive; and there was a careless elegance and charm about him that enchanted me as much in London as it had in Melbourne. I found that I was more in love with him than I had thought. Just as it had in Australia, the realization disturbed me.

Frequently Edward would take me to dine at the Café Royal, then the meeting place of London's intellectual circles. There I first saw Somerset Maugham, monocled and impeccable in evening dress; the equally dandified writer and theatrical critic, Max Beerbohm, and the red-bearded George Bernard Shaw, whose clothes were a revelation to me. They were hand-knitted by Jaeger!

It was at the Café Royal that Edward proposed to me for the second time. This time I did not hesitate. In a sudden, almost frightening onrush of decision I accepted him. We were married quietly, at a Registry Office in London, with only two of our closest friends as witnesses. It was very private and very tender. I recall that we lunched afterward at the Savoy Grill, which in those days was the thing to do. Edward ordered plovers' eggs with champagne, although I was so excited that it wouldn't have mattered to me what I ate.

Our honeymoon was spent at Nice. During the first few days I lived in a haze of happiness. I had never before been to the South of France. That unbelievably lovely country had not yet begun to be exploited, and we took many long, leisurely drives in the hills around Grasse, to Monte Carlo, and as far as Cannes, which was then a small fishing village. I was almost inclined to believe Edward when he said smilingly, "All this beauty has been arranged especially for you and me, Helena."

A honeymoon should be one of the happiest times in a girl's life, but before ours was over, Edward and I had had our first serious quarrel. It was my fault. Walking into the hotel lobby one morning to join Edward, I saw him talking and laughing with a very pretty young girl. He was so engrossed in his conversation with her that he seemed totally unaware of my presence. Overwhelmed by jealousy, I rushed out and for no reason at all hastened into the nearest jeweler's shop, where I bought myself an expensive string of pearls! Then I hailed a passing hansom cab and told the driver to take me to the station. I had only one idea—to get away. Without giving Edward a chance to say a word of explanation, I caught the next train to Paris. He followed me there, and by the time he had caught up with me, I deeply regretted having behaved so foolishly. (I kept the pearls, however, and subsequently, whenever we quarreled over anything, I would go out and buy more pearls. Buying "quarrel" jewelry is one of my weaknesses. Some women buy hats, but I am more extravagant in anger, as I am in most things.)

We returned to London for the opening of the Grafton Street salon. But this time the sign that hung outside the premises was painted by a skilled professional, and under the name, Helena Rubinstein, there appeared in smaller letters, the words "Salon de Beauté Valaze"—my trademark for many years to come.

Edward and I made our first home together on the third floor of the Grafton Street building, over the salon. (My "kitchen" was tucked away in the attic.) The apartment was light and airy, with a view of the city for miles around, and Edward was delighted with it. Here he could do his writing undisturbed. Since he had a great flair for the creative, I welcomed his ideas and consulted with him on every business problem.

Press receptions were still unknown and I had not yet begun to advertise, although Edward urged me to do so. The only thing was to wait until personal recommendations sent clients to me. I knew that sooner or later they would come. I had learned to be patient.

It was then around 1908. Make-up was used exclusively for stage purposes, and actresses were the only women who knew anything of the art or who would dare to be seen in public wearing anything but the lightest film of rice powder. Gabrielle Ray was probably the most advanced exponent of make-up. She had discovered that shading at the corners of the nostrils (she used red and mauve dots) could refine the appearance of her nose and that a little shadow on the eyelids and over the temples enhanced the size and luminosity of her eyes. She would put a touch of red on her cheeks and then, with a hare's-foot dipped in terra-cotta powder, touch up the lobes of her ears and the tip of her chin. But make-up as it was to develop was unheard of outside the world of the theater, although I experimented privately and learned many valuable lessons from stage personalities, which in turn I taught to a few of my more daring clients. They spread the word, and I knew that another beauty barrier would soon be toppled.

At the salon I specialized in skin analysis and facial treatments, but in my "kitchen" on the topmost floor of the Grafton Street building I had begun to experiment with the formulation of make-up preparations. I detested the chalk-white "rice powder" then in vogue. It had originated in China, of milled rice, and it made every woman look as though her face had been newly whitewashed. Color

41

was the only answer. A rosy, pink-tinted face powder seemed the most logical start, and for fair-skinned blondes a shade of rachel. I wanted, too, to introduce faint but distinctive perfumes into my preparations, so that they would be immediately identifiable through their lovely subtle fragrances. All this would take time, however. The world was still highly conservative, and to break with tradition would not be easy for most women, I knew. I must not be too ambitious too soon.

Here, as in Melbourne, curiosity brought my first clients. Ladies who had visited the house when it was Lord Salisbury's home were eager to see what "horrors" I had committed in renovating it. But such frank curiosity would have been considered extremely vulgar and beneath them. They came despite it, but each was anxious that her friends should know nothing of her visit. More than once I watched from an upstairs window as one of them arrived, alone, in a covered carriage which dropped her discreetly at the corner of Grafton Street. There, with her veil lowered, she would wait for a few moments in Bruton Lane, out of sight she thought, until the street was free of passers-by. Then came the last few hurried steps to the salon. Each of the ladies was dressed in the height of fashion, with white kid gloves to the elbow and carrying a small gold mesh bag containing a gold pencil, a perfumed handkerchief, and a flat gold case for visiting cards. Money was rarely included; a lady never carried money.

More than once I wondered what would have happened if any two of my furtive visitors had stepped simultaneously from their carriages and recognized one another! But all that mattered was that they came—and then came again and again.

My fee was ten guineas for a course of twelve beauty treatments, and I charged what was then the equivalent of $2,000 for regular weekly visits the year round. An unheard of innovation! Yet within a year of the opening of my London salon I had over a thousand clients on my books, on the annual basis. There was no need for me to worry any longer about the rent.

One of my first clients, who bore a great English name, had suffered for years with acute acne. The condition of her skin had made her almost a recluse. One day she walked into the salon, heavily veiled, and shyly asked to see me in private. It took a little time to persuade her to enter the consultation room, and as I helped her to remove her veil, I saw for the first time her dreadful skin pitifully disguised under a blanket of white powder.

In Vienna I had learned of a new and then daring peeling treatment for seriously blemished skins such as hers. To try this would be her only hope, and I finally persuaded her to accept the treatment from Dr. List. Once I had convinced her, she cooperated conscientiously, and for six months she came to the salon each week—nervous about this still new treatment, yet she came. Gradually, as the pitted outer surface of the skin was removed and the new, young tissue underneath became visible, she was able to see for herself the beginnings of a transformation. As her skin grew softer and lovelier, so did her entire attitude toward life. She was no longer a shy, hurt, tragic woman. All the natural warmth and charm which had been obscured by her unhappiness and self-consciousness came to the surface. Her gratitude was touching and inspiring.

Through her introductions a whole procession of her friends came to me. A year later, when she went to India with her husband, she sent me a number of Indian princesses, many with lovely features, but who were forced to hide their dreadful skins behind thick veils. I loved to see these colorful creatures in my salon, small-boned and graceful, and adorned with superb jewels. Around their necks they wore magnificent strands of pearls; their wrists and hands were covered with emeralds and rubies.

So my reputation in London grew. The society magazines took to mentioning my salon in their editorial pages, and this set Edward to writing clever advertising—another innovation in that day.

After successfully completing my first experiments with skin-toned face powder, the next step was rouge. Only Margot Asquith had the courage to use it openly. I taught her how to accentuate her remarkable features, to look even more striking. She was delighted, and her frankly enthusiastic replies to all who admired her brought the finest unpaid publicity I could have hoped to find.

Mrs. Asquith insisted on inviting me to her home, where I met other well-known personalities, many of them her

43

fellow members in "The Souls," that coterie of intellectu-
ally and artistically minded aristocrats, Bohemians, and
statesmen who recognized no political or social barriers.

The social life I was living in London at that time was
far different from anything I had ever imagined in my
wildest dreams as a girl in Cracow. Baroness d'Erlanger,
leader of one section of society, became a friend of mine.
She lived in Byron's old house in Piccadilly, and there I
met yet another cross section of the artistic and literary
world. "I am interested in what people are," was her attitude, "not in who they are." This is the accepted attitude today among all thinking people, but there was a
time when it was considered quite daring.

Baroness d'Erlanger and I had a common interest in
interior decoration and we enjoyed sharing our ideas on
the subject. Her rooms were all white and gold, walls,
furnishings, and flowers, and she had launched a fashion
for baroque Venetian furniture which I admired and emu-
lated. Mrs. Syrie Maugham, Somerset Maugham's talented
decorator wife, was to make this trend widely popular in
the thirties, but like so many fads in decoration its very
popularity became its undoing.

Catherine d'Erlanger was one of the first sophisticated
originals who lived on an international scale. She was truly
avant-garde, and her taste and complete confidence in it
and herself permitted her to create about her an atmosphere of rare excitement. For many years she lived in
Venice where her Palladian villa was filled with her artist
friends. Invariably they would be set to work redecorating
her rooms from the wide assortment of bric-a-brac she
loved to collect. With World War II she was forced to
move to the States, where she made her home in California.
She opened a night club on the famous Sunset Strip, in
Hollywood, and as an exotic she attracted to her club
many celebrities. It was not unusual for her to sit at the
cash register in an evening gown and emeralds—with her
feet in a pair of tennis shoes. And with complete aplomb!
My last memory of this extraordinary woman was at a
party given in her small home in Hollywood. She sat surrounded by her paintings, her Venetian furniture and her
nine cats, gaily entertaining a lively group of devoted
friends. Stravinsky was there with Aldous Huxley, Cole

Porter, and Cary Grant. She preferred the company of men and made no bones about it, but I had been asked and so had Greta Garbo. We were the only two women present—both of us silent!

Edward liked nothing better than to be with creative people and to have them around him in his home. No matter how much writing he had done during the day, he was ready when the evening came to entertain or be entertained. We gave buffet suppers and dinners to which were asked young artists and writers. Our parties were gay, relaxed, and quite informal.

We continued to go out a great deal, and it was at a Polish diplomatic reception that I first met young Artur Rubinstein. He was then only twenty years old, but after a successful debut in the U.S., he was already recognized as a great pianist. He and I had both been born in Poland. We were both Jewish. We were both members of large families, I the eldest of eight, and Artur the youngest of seven. Because we shared the same name we liked to think there was some family tie between us but, in fact, we have never been able to trace a common ancestry. He is a man who emanates great warmth, and from our first meeting I was very much drawn to him. One evening, almost hesitant of my own boldness, I asked him to my home to play for my guests. He accepted, and we have been friends ever since.

Artur has a wonderful philosophy, and apart from his marvelous playing, I love to hear him talk. "The most important thing in life is to realize why one is alive," I have heard him say. "It is not only to build bridges and tall buildings, or to make money, but to do something truly important, to do something for humanity."

Diplomatic functions such as the one at which I first met Artur Rubinstein led to social calls in Mayfair, and soon Edward and I were receiving invitations to attend more formal balls and weekend parties. I had now started seriously to learn the art of entertaining.

I tried to give the most perfect buffet suppers I could devise. I cared very little for the pompous dinners we frequently attended, all seated around a long table with one man to every woman regardless of whether we had any interests in common. Instead, in our home Edward and I had a round table which would seat twelve comfortably. When numbers were larger, we added several smaller round tables, with no set seating arrangements.

In this way it was possible to spot the slightest sign of boredom in a guest or to suggest a change of seats while the next course was being chosen from the buffet. Then, as now, I used my imagination. I had several different dinner services and I would mix them all up for visual effect. At each table I planned a complete color scheme. If I was using a yellow cloth, I would choose orange opaline plates and pale-green cut glass for the table, which was decorated with a low bowl of magenta anemones. For a more exotic effect I used black Japanese lacquer dishes with red Bohemian glass. Sometimes, as a *tour de force*, I would match the food to the color scheme, serving an all-pink meal of salmon, followed by saignant roast beef, and then strawberry mousse on pink plates, with a vin rosé in large terra-cotta beakers.

I have always preferred a simple menu. In the early days in London our artist friends especially enjoyed my Polish suppers on cold winter nights. There would be steaming Polish vegetable soups and the sour cream invariably to be found on our family table at home, with piping hot meat rolls, *piroshki*, fish stews, and other typically Polish dishes, well seasoned and cooked in red wine with dill and other herbs.

With such a full social life it may sound as though my business was being neglected. But I have never let the business side of my life slip. Fortunately sleep has never been important to me. I often worked in my "kitchen" way into the night, even after a party, until I could no longer keep my eyes open! Then I would creep downstairs and to sleep, without waking Edward.

While directing the operations in London, I remained in constant touch with Ceska and the Australian business. In the meantime, though, a growing number of inquiries and orders had begun to come in from the Continent. Here was an excuse for me to plan another visit to Paris with Edward. Apart from business, it would give me the opportunity to buy some new clothes. What remained of my trousseau dresses were becoming much too well known among the friends and acquaintances we were seeing almost nightly.

Before 1914 a couturier dress was priced between $150 and $250. For another $100 the most exquisite hand embroideries and beading could be had. My favorite dressmaker of the period was Paul Poiret, a jovial, bearded Frenchman whose genius was expressed in the daring originality of his designs. His origins were humble, but he had the gift of making every woman feel beautiful and extravagant.

Son of the owner of a small textile business, Poiret had first been apprenticed to an umbrella maker. With the small bits of silk left over from the umbrellas he took to dressing children's dolls in the oriental fashion. What had begun as a hobby soon captivated him entirely, and he left the umbrella maker to join the workrooms of the then famous designer, Doucet, from whom he learned the secrets of fine dressmaking. From Doucet, Poiret graduated to the house of Worth, where I first met him, and shortly thereafter he proceeded to open his own establishment.

Poiret was an idealist, a dreamer, but he was also a fashion tyrant. He was the first man to wage war on the corset. "Like all revolutions," he said gaily, "mine is in the name of Liberty . . . I hereby free the bosom and the waistline." And then he proceeded to shackle women's legs with his hobble skirt!

I hated the first dress Poiret made for me, and I told him so. He was furious, and as I stepped out of the dress he snatched it from me and tore it into ribbons. "If you don't like it," he said, "you need never wear it." But he came to understand my needs and the type of clothes I felt to be right for me (with my 4 feet 10 inches I looked ridiculous in a hobble skirt), and he made me some of the most beautiful clothes I have ever owned.

Whenever I was in Paris I would make it a point to visit Poiret, not only to see his newest collection but to enjoy his outspoken opinions on everything and everybody and to call on him at his extraordinary flat. Daylight and the smell of fresh air meant nothing to him. He was strongly influenced by Asiatic art, and he lived in overcrowded, lamp-lit rooms filled with innumerable Chinese screens, rococco furniture, and Venetian mirrors. He was a person who came alive only at night.

Frankly an exotic, it pleased Poiret to receive his personal friends (at least those who dared come) with live panthers chained in the entrance hall, each one attended by a six-foot Negro stripped to the waist, a bejeweled turban wound around his head, and his bare torso oiled and gleaming to resemble statuary.

When Edward and I returned to London, my new Poiret clothes created a sensation. A striking, exciting wardrobe is a necessity to a woman in the beauty business. But by then I wanted more than a new wardrobe. I was fired with an ambition to open a Salon de Beauté in Paris. France had come to hold for me somewhat the same fascination and allure that England had had when I was in Melbourne, and the old restlessness gnawed at me.

In the spring of 1909, however, I discovered I was going to have a child. I had not consciously longed for motherhood, perhaps because I had been so busy always, but the reality of carrying a child stirred deep emotions in me. Edward, too, was jubilant, and he surrounded me with a thousand attentions. My body bloomed, and so did my spirits. Never had I felt more energetic.

The apartment on the top floor, above the salon in Grafton Street, was no longer suitable as a residence. With a baby on the way, we set about finding a real home, quite separate from my offices. I wanted a house with a garden, and we made inquiries about country properties. In Roehampton Lane, near Putney Heath, outside London, we found a large, comfortable Victorian house mysteriously called Solna. It stood in a private park previously owned by J. Pierpont Morgan, the American banker.

Already my head was filled with plans for decorating and "modernizing," but for the first time in my life these plans were centered around a home rather than a business.

The house had twenty rooms and three unused Victorian hothouses attached. The hothouses were a problem, since neither Edward nor I intended to cultivate exotic flowers or grow vegetables under glass. It was Edward's suggestion that we should turn them into extra sitting rooms, which was what we did.

Each room of the house was decorated in a different

style, and passing from one room to another was like moving through some of the most creative epochs the world has known. A Chinese Chippendale room adjoined a Louis XIII room which, in turn, was followed by an Empire room, and so on. I planned a nautical nursery with cabin fittings and porthole windows—gambling, accurately, that our firstborn would be a boy. One large room was transformed into a library for Edward, another into a conventional billiard room.

Still under the influence of the extravagant colors which I had so loved in the Ballet Russe I devised color schemes for the new house which were glowing and alive. Some were a trifle too much even for Edward at first. He complained that magenta and gold together made him feel dizzy. But by contrast, there was his library and the billiard room, restful, subdued, and soothing.

My greatest triumph was with the hothouses. As Edward had suggested, they were transformed into sitting rooms. In one, which he called my "Scheherazade" room, a real fountain played in the center, cushions were piled on the floor, and large comfortable couches lined the walls. There were flowering plants everywhere, and these garden rooms were extremely popular with our friends. We made the most of every bit of winter sunshine, and during the summer months the hothouse-sitting rooms, shaded by melon-colored blinds, were cool and inviting.

Edward had now turned from writing to book publishing. This produced an influx of new faces in our home, and we were constantly surrounded with people. One of our most frequent visitors was Jacob Epstein, the sculptor. He first introduced me to African sculpture, which appealed to me greatly, and under his tutelage I became an avid collector. Whenever I was planning a visit to Paris he would give me catalogs of the African collections to be auctioned there, marking the finest pieces so that I would know what to bid for. My enthusiasm often went beyond his suggestions, but prices were low then and the range of objects extraordinary.

As my collection grew, few of our friends cared for it. "How strange," they would say, "to think of someone who has dedicated her life to beauty, buying such ugly things." It was not until years later, when the paintings of Juan

49

Gris, Picasso, and Modigliani began to receive world-wide recognition, that African primitive sculpture came into its own as a source of their inspiration. How wisely Jacob Epstein had advised me. I had always favored the unusual, and when I followed such sound advice as his, as well as my own "inner eye," my purchases were invariably good.

4 } Paris–New York

ONCE my plans for a new home in England were a reality, and life at Solna was running smoothly, the dream of opening a salon in Paris began to nag at me. I was awaiting the birth of my first child, but pregnancy in no way prevented me from making plans or from continuing with my usual activities. I was in excellent health—in fact, I had never felt better—and Edward encouraged me to do whatever made me happy.

My sister, Manka, was established with me in London. She had energy, ability, and charm, and her assistance was invaluable. Manka was a born manager and an enthusiastic teacher, and with her in charge of Grafton Street my mind was completely at ease.

By now I had many French clients, but they were no longer satisfied with having to write to me in London for advice and help. They wanted the personal attention which, with the sale of my creams, had become the very essence of my business.

As it happened, on one of my frequent visits to Paris I called on my old friend and teacher, Dr. Berthelot, to exchange a little gossip and to keep up with the latest dovelopments in dermatology. He, too, urged me to open a Paris salon. "French women are practical, Helena," he said, "but they also adore luxuries. You can meet them on both these levels. Your scientific approach will satisfy their practicality, while your products and the ambiance of your salon will feed their craving for luxury!"

Dr. Berthelot proceeded to introduce me to a Russian beautician whom he knew, Madame Chambaron. Her husband was far less understanding than my Edward. He had told her bluntly that she must choose between him and her career. She had chosen her husband and decided to sell her business. I was more than interested in her decision and I told her so. We soon agreed on the terms, signed the necessary papers, and before the birth of my son Roy, I became the owner of an excellent line of herbal preparations and a salon in the rue St. Honoré.

The time had come for another sister to join me. I wrote home to Cracow and this time it was Pauline who took over in Paris while I returned to Solna, to await the arrival of the baby. The Australian business was running smoothly in the capable hands of Ceska. Manka had the London salon under complete control. With Pauline in Paris looking after my new French interests, I could retire to have my baby, pleased that I had realized yet another of my ambitions.

Three months later Roy was born. It was an easy birth, but I admit that when he was put into my arms, red-faced and wrinkled, I wondered how nature could start us all off looking so old and so troubled. Within a few days, of course, I thought him the most beautiful creature in the world.

Edward and I were delighted with our son. We now had all we could possibly want of life, and from the time of Roy's birth in 1909 until a year or more after the arrival of my second son Horace, in 1912, I spent more time at home than in all the years to follow. They were the happy, peaceful years, and I often think back on life at Solna with yearning. The lovely comfortable Victorian house, the nursery teas with the boys, the evenings of gaiety with Edward and our friends—all of these memories fill me with nostalgia.

When I say sometimes that the beauty business has always come first with me, I must make an exception of those years. Yet even while I lived them, happy to see the children growing straight and strong, enjoying each moment as it passed, there was a nagging feeling of something missing. Had I grown so accustomed to battling the daily obstacles of business that I could not enjoy the pleasures of domesticity for which millions of other women yearned? I chided myself for my restlessness. Nevertheless when my younger son Horace was about two, and an independent little boy, I suggested to Edward that we all move to Paris. It bothered me that I had never properly launched my Salon de Beauté there. Fortunately Edward was by nature a "citizen of the world," or perhaps there was something of the gypsy in both of us, for he welcomed the idea and before long he had found a home for us in Montparnasse —the first of our Paris apartments.

Once the family had settled down in our new quarters, I threw myself into the excitement of really launching the French business and into the gaiety of Parisian life.

Luckily I found a great woman friend to guide and advise me when we moved to Paris. I had known of Misia Nathanson through mutual friends in Poland, and I looked her up. Our common interest in art became an immediate link, and our husbands also became friends. Some years later when she married the painter José Maria Sert, Misia became famous in her own right as a patroness of artists and writers. She entertained lavishly and mixed her guests freely in the hope that her artist friends might meet future patrons. I was visiting her one day, and after I had admired a new portrait that Bonnard had just completed of Misia sitting in her sunlit drawing room, we sat gossiping over endless glasses of Russian tea. Suddenly she said: "Helena, you should entertain here in Paris. It will make you less shy in speaking French and this will help you with your clients." Then she added, "I always receive guests on Thursdays; you must give your parties on Sundays. But to do it regularly—that is the secret of being a good hostess."

I felt that I was still too new to life in Paris for anything quite so elaborate. But Misia organized all the details, even making lists of the guests I was to invite to my first Paris "At Home."

The first Sunday came. All of my guests turned up. But I drifted about miserably, convinced that the evening was a failure. The men scarcely spoke to the women; they merely looked at them across the room, asking endless questions about them of one another—questions which I felt were entirely out of place. No one was more surprised than I when the same group turned up again on the following Sunday. But Misia convinced me that in Paris all that was asked of a successful hostess was an ample supply of good food and wine and enough pretty women to look at and talk about. A most peculiar arrangement, I thought.

My clients at the salon represented current Parisian society. Their names on my books read like pages out of a fashion magazine. The leading members of the aristocracy, the stage and the arts were all my faithful customers. I was happy enough with my life, with the excitement of success and with the promise of what the future might bring . . . yet I was still searching for something new.

I had heard of Swedish massage, but I had never had the time or the patience to try it. For those Parisian women with leisure to enjoy it, however, I was convinced it would be something they would find beneficial and relaxing. For a long time I had kept the idea in the back of my mind, until one day I actually met a wonderful Swedish masseuse. I hired Tilla on the spot, although inwardly I hoped it would not prove too difficult to persuade French women to accept the benefits of body massage. What if they should prove to be prudish, I wondered.

Madame Colette, who today holds a most distinguished place in French literature, unwittingly helped to make the treatments popular. The rumor had leaked out that the pen name, "Willy," disguised her true identity. And "Willy" was the most successful French author of the day! Apparently Colette's husband, Monsieur Willy, himself a second-rate writer, would lock her in her room and force her to write book after book—which he claimed as his own! Seeking some form of escape and relaxation, Colette, who had fewer then the usual inhibitions, would take advantage of the opportunity whenever her husband was away to rush over to the salon and enjoy a soothing massage.

When she was about to leave after her first visit, she

took me aside to whisper in that throaty voice which could be heard and recognized by everyone in the salon, "Never have I felt so wonderful! Now I am ready for anything . . . even for my husband!" Soon her words were repeated all over town, and from that time on Tilla's appointment book was completely filled.

Paris was now my home in every sense of the word. I had lovely French clothes, many friends, a comfortable house, a successful business—and yet I was restless. A new interest began to absorb me. Always a collector of one thing or another, I had taken to collecting paintings, in particular the abstract works then beginning to emerge from the studios of Picasso, Juan Gris, and Braque. Edward was fully absorbed with his literary work and perfectly happy. Then, in August 1914, war was declared.

It was heartbreaking for me to see so many splendid young men cheerfully marching off to Verdun and then, in the following months, to have to face their mothers and widows with words of sympathy and compassion.

We stayed on in Paris until the beginning of 1915 when Edward, an American citizen, persuaded me that we had to go to America for the sake of our sons, who had their father's nationality. Leaving Europe meant forsaking everything I had built over the years, to begin a completely new life in a strange country. Even my habitual optimism and determination failed me. How could I foresee that in the United States I was to find greater opportunities than ever before and that in this new world I was to know the fulfillment of all my dreams in the development of the beauty business? I cannot pretend that I enjoyed the voyage from France to America, in spite of the fact that Edward and the boys were with me. The ship was crowded beyond belief; the sea was rough, and the constant threat of enemy submarines added to my anxiety.

I had left everything behind me, my memories of struggle and success, my homes, my business, my friends. But what concerned me most was being separated by a vast ocean and half of Europe from my parents in Poland. I had had no news of them since the declaration of war, and all my efforts to communicate with them had failed.

G. K. Chesterton once said that most Americans are "born drunk—drunk on a sort of invisible champagne that

55

wells up from within." The invisible champagne is really there; you breathe it in with the air. There is a constant spirit of youth and hope in the U.S.A. which has enormously stimulated me since the day I first arrived. It seemed as if I had stepped out of a world bound by tradition into one where the past was of little consequence. Only the present and the future really counted.

We arrived in New York on a bitterly cold day in January 1915 after our nerve-racking sailing. The first thing I noticed was the whiteness of the women's faces and the oddly grayish color of their lips. Only their noses, mauve with cold, seemed to stand out.

The Gibson girl, created by Charles Dana Gibson, the illustrator, was the model of American propriety and beauty. Her creed was modesty, and to the average American male she was an aloof dream girl. Only women described as "loose" used make-up; "nice girls" sprinkled a little rice powder on their noses and beyond that trusted in God to make them beautiful.

So, I said to myself, here is not only a new country but a huge new market for my products. I breathed nothing of this to Edward, however. First we would have to find a home in this great new country, a school for the boys, and attend to the infinite details of establishing our lives here.

Edward found the perfect house for us in Greenwich, Connecticut. On an unbelievably lovely spring day we drove out to see it, motoring along the Hudson River and then north to Westchester, where masses of golden forsythia lined the roadside. It seemed to me that I had never known such a glorious spring anywhere, and as we drove up to the house, on old Indian Chase Road, I was ready to fall in love with it on the spot, though I had no idea what the house was like. It boasted few architectural pretensions, since the style was 1910—Tudor. But I have known few country houses with the same degree of comfort and coziness, and the grounds suggested all the charm of carefully landscaped gardens. It has remained my American country home ever since, with the sunlight a constant companion, brightening every room and dappling the tree-shaded lawns down to the lake where my sons sailed their boats as children. Ten minutes away there is the beach where Roy and Horace first learned to swim, in Long Island Sound. In these happy surroundings the children had no difficulty settling down to the American way of life.

During the year that followed we were busy planning, making changes here and there, and furnishing the house; but my dream of a great new market for my products in the States had not left me, and soon after the year was up my first American Salon de Beauté was opened in New York City on West Forty-ninth Street, in a type of building known as "a brownstone."

The walls of the salon were covered in dark-blue velvet, with rose-colored baseboards; the period furnishings were upholstered in pale-blue silk, and the rooms were decorated with the works of the Polish sculptor, Elie Nadelman. The opulence of the surroundings pleased my customers, and journalists wrote exciting articles about the new salon with its amazing décor. No amount of newspaper advertising could have brought about the same results.

There is no denying that the beauty business is made up of part theater, part glamor, on the surface at least; and I admit that I was the first to insist upon these trappings. But women, I feel, love a hint of mystery and of glamour —as what man does not?

It seems strange to think that only fifty years ago American men were quite puritanical and their women excessively modest. The whole country was struggling to acquire an air of social respectability, largely to efface the memories of a raucous, brawling, pioneering past. Such a small matter as the use of lipstick remained a moral issue for many years, and rouge became popular when women discovered that it could also be used secretly to give their lips a touch of color. But Puritanism and Victorianism crumbled when America entered the war, and American doughboys returned from Europe with a new concept of emancipated women.

Many have been the strange quirks of fate that determined my life, but none is so strange as the fact that I should have come to the States because of circumstances beyond my control—and arrived in this land filled with opportunity at exactly the right time.

I started to advertise, discreetly at first, stressing the scientific explanation of any claims I made for my preparations. Those early advertisements, now considered quaint and old-fashioned, still serve as my bible today. During that first hot summer one of my earliest ads urged women to protect their skins from the scorching rays of the sun, and it read:

Freckling and Sunburn can be prevented. Helena Rubinstein promises to obviate the annoyance that women with sensitive skins suffer from exposure to the sun.

Underneath, there appeared the following words:

This is a strong statement and could scarcely be made by any other person than Madame Helena Rubinstein. Her unique position as an authority in beauty and its culture is recognized universally. The same Madame Rubinstein numbers among the clientele who patronize her London and Paris establishments, known as "Maisons de Beauté Valaze," many famous beauties and women of the highest rank in European courts.

After this came the scientific explanation:

It is an established fact that sunlight is composed of rays of different colors and amongst these are blue rays and violet rays. Whoever takes an interest in photography comes across these rays under the name of "actinic" rays. They produce the image on the sensitive photographic plate in the same way as they also produce freckles, tan the face, the hands or the arms. If you shut out these rays when you develop your film or plate, you can debar them from staining and browning the skin and complexion.

I wonder what reception such an advertisement would have today? I cannot imagine advertising agents either in Europe or America submitting such copy for my approval now. However, there is no doubt that it conveyed the message, for it was not long before that one salon in New York became insufficient for such a vast country.

How I longed for Manka to be with me then. As children we had been very close, and we understood one another. I needed her help, and I wrote to her in London, asking if she would join me in America. By the next mail I had her reply, and I could barely wait until she was with me two months later.

It was wartime, and American women, with all their new responsibilities, were becoming more aware of themselves. Together Manka and I made plans, bold plans. We were two foreigners in a new country, but the thought of obstacles never seemed to enter our minds. By 1917 there were Rubinstein salons in San Francisco, Boston, and Philadelphia, and I was busy negotiating for premises in other cities. Shortly afterward we were established in Washington, Chicago, and Toronto.

Suddenly we were faced with a new situation. Department stores began clamoring for the right to sell my preparations over the counter. At first I hesitated. The girls in my salons were fully trained. They knew all about the preparations they were selling. They were competent to advise women, making sure that only those preparations were purchased which were right for the client's particular needs. Mass sales by unqualified assistants might jeopardize the Rubinstein reputation and result in unsatisfied clients. However, as the demands increased, it became impossible to ignore them.

As a first step, to keep the sales of my preparations exclusive, we accepted only substantial orders from well-known stores. When we received an acceptable order I would personally travel to the store, wherever it was (usually accompanied by Manka), to train the salespeople in my method of introducing, promoting, and selling my preparations. I did not realize what I was letting myself in for!

Our first customer was the famous department store in San Francisco, The City of Paris. By the time our deliveries were made to The City of Paris other important department stores had followed their lead, and to keep my word that I would train all salesgirls personally I set out on a cross-country instructional tour. In the stores Manka and I gave courses and lectures to the sales staff and private consultations to customers.

Gradually the use of cosmetics came to be accepted in the States, but there were still many women who believed that a single cold cream was all that was necessary for the care and nourishing of the skin. At night we trained the assistants to be beauty consultants and teachers, giving them a sound knowledge of my preparations and their use, to be imparted to their assistants and to customers. For eighteen out of every twenty-four hours we were either traveling between one city and another or actively working. We lived out of our suitcases like actresses in a theatrical touring company. But with the excitement and stimulus we were never conscious of being tired.

Manka and I made it a point to wear the clothes we had brought over with us from Paris. We were well aware that many women came to see what we were wearing—and we really gave them something to look at. After one appearance at Jordan Marsh, in conservative Boston, the following mention appeared in the morning newspaper: "Madame Rubinstein wore a tomato-colored dress and eight strands of black pearls. Eight hundred women were enraptured by her lecture on treating the skin and on make-up for formal occasions."

Oddly enough, the fact that I was of Polish birth and had spent much of my life in Europe gave me unexpected glamor. I suspected that my accent and my clothes intrigued my audience more than anything I said; but they came in droves, listened, and then bought our preparations. Whatever their reasons for coming, we taught them a great deal and this, more than anything, established our reputation.

The technique established on that first tour was followed successfully by Manka for many years, and it remains the foundation on which my niece, Mala Rubinstein, still plans every traveling event. At regular intervals all department stores carrying the Rubinstein range of beauty preparations are visited by one of Mala's trained beauty consultants to demonstrate our newest products. There are also qualified consultants at every counter to teach women how to use our different kinds of make-up and to advise each of them on the preparations suited to her skin. With more than five hundred Rubinstein preparations now on the market, this is an essential service to customers.

Business was booming in the States. This was the era when a number of stars of the theater and silent movies made front-page news by launching new beauty trends.

For Theda Bara, "the Siren of the Silent Screen," we helped to create "The Vamp" look which became internationally famous. Enthusiastic fans copied her hair styles, her clothes, and her mannerisms. Her eyes were amazingly beautiful, but camera techniques were not as advanced as they are now and much of their beauty was lost on the screen. She came to me to find a way of emphasizing them.

Eye make-up of any kind was unknown in America. Mascara had been used only in France by a few stage personalities, and not always well. But with my love for the theater and my insatiable curiosity, I had delved into the beauty secrets of several French actresses. I had also experimented with kohl (the original eye make-up invented by the ancient Egyptians and used by Cleopatra). For Theda Bara I made a mascara which drew attention to her lovely eyes so that they dominated her whole face—and the mascara did not streak! I also added a touch of color to her eyelids. The effect was tremendously dramatic. It was a sensation reported in every newspaper and magazine—only little less of a sensation than when Theda Bara first painted her toenails!

America had been good to me. The boys were happily settled at boarding school. My American staff was well trained. Best of all, the war had come to an end. Suddenly the desire to see Europe was strong in me. As soon as the Armistice was signed in November 1918 Edward and I began making plans to return to Paris. We gave no thought as to whether our stay was to be long or short. Friends . . . business . . . the home we had left so hurriedly there . . . everything was calling us back.

5 { Marriage Versus Business

It was good to be on board ship again, bound for France, and enjoying our first real vacation in years. Edward and I talked, we laughed, we played bridge, the thought of business very far from our minds. Then one day I picked up a French newspaper from a nearby deck chair. A small advertisement caught my eye, announcing an old house for sale in the Faubourg St. Honoré. I immediately cabled for details and by nightfall had bought the five-story building outright, while I was still crossing the Atlantic Ocean. Pauline, who had been left in charge of the French business, had often written to complain that the existing salon there was much too small. With the war at an end, I felt that the time had come to expand the French business.

In 1918, with the lifting of the terrible tensions and tragedies of war, London and Paris were lighthearted and gay. We visited both cities and found the people almost frantically determined to get the most out of life. In the night clubs the dance craze was at its height, with the charming young Irene and Vernon Castle the rage of Europe. Everyone was doing the tango, the two-step, and the fox trot. But the atmosphere of enforced gaiety was something I found difficult to share, perhaps because the habit of work had by then become the pattern of my life.

Edward was happy to be back in Paris, where he was soon involved in new literary endeavors; and I had my salon at 52, Rue du Faubourg St. Honoré, to be decorated and refurnished. We had never had a real home of our own in Paris. Until then we had been living over the salon. But we both felt that it was no longer what we wanted. At Edward's suggestion we arranged for the building of an apartment house at 216, Boulevard Raspail, on the Left Bank, in the heart of the literary and artistic center of the city. On one floor of the building, we decided, we would establish a real home, where we would be free to enjoy the companionship of family and friends without worrying about business. Edward also thought it would be an excellent idea to include a private theater on the ground floor, so that some of the talented young playwrights he was befriending could see their works performed before a select audience. This is what we did. After the scripts had been read and auditions held, each of the plays was produced in English, French and Italian. I had always loved the theater, and we enjoyed many delightful evenings there—until, unfortunately, the police intervened. They alleged that some of the plays were too outspoken and that the playwrights (whether we recognized it or not) were using our private stage to attack the government! The theater was closed by order of the Prefecture, although it is used to this day as a cinema.

This was my only encounter with the law as a "political revolutionary"—although I never could understand what it was the government objected to in the plays, and I still believe they were overly impulsive about the whole thing.

We renewed old friendships at the buffet supper parties I enjoyed giving and, as before, artists and writers were our most frequent guests. Edward's literary projects were progressing, and under his influence I had begun seriously to collect paintings. My interest in fine old furniture was also growing, guided by a young friend, Christian Dior, who then owned a small antique shop.

The early twenties were stimulating years for modern art and for the artists living in Paris. The first of the great painters of our century whom I was privileged to meet was Henri Matisse. I found him cold, aloof, and difficult to deal with. I admired his work, yet whenever I wanted to buy one of the paintings I saw in his studio, he immediately referred me to his dealer. This irritated me. I have always preferred buying directly from the artist.

Edward and I loved to sit at the Dome, a restaurant in Montparnasse near our home, where it was not unusual to see Amedeo Modigliani go by in his shabby velvet suit, hawking his paintings from table to table. I was intrigued with his work, with the long oval faces, the simplified features, the curved necks influenced by African sculpture. I bought several of his paintings and a portfolio of his drawings, but Modigliani was far from communicative, longing only for the oblivion of drink. His unhappy smile expressed far more of his feelings than the few words we exchanged. Life no longer held any magic for him, and he was soon to die prematurely.

In no time at all our home was crowded with the new wave of young painters, sculptors, and writers, all emerging from the compulsory hibernation of the war. They were anxiously searching for commissions and for the opportunity to show their work. Among them was Marc Chagall. He was a young, slender electric eel of a man, with bright eyes and an unruly mop of hair. His humor and zest for life were contagious. After a few glasses of wine he would burst into Russian songs or tell funny stories in Yiddish which none of the other guests could understand. He was such a masterful clown, however, that his miming and dancing assured the success of any party he attended. Sometimes he would come by with Braque or Dufy, but more often he was accompanied by a young Polish painter named Marcoussis, whose work I especially favored.

Edward and I saw a great deal of Marcoussis and his wife. He was warm, intelligent, with an eye for good painting. His own work suffered from this critical sense, although since his death he has become recognized and appreciated by knowing collectors. With Marcoussis we would go from one artist's studio to another, and to further my education, he often urged me to visit galleries with him. "Now, there's a painting to have," he would say. "It's a beautiful picture, and one day it will be worth a fortune." He said this so often that I did not always react. What a pity! If I had followed his advice, my collection today would be better than it is, and I would own some of the most exciting modern paintings in the world.

I did buy a good deal, though, from both artists and galleries. Besides following the advice of knowledgeable friends as to the paintings I should purchase, there was also a spark in me that ignited when I saw a picture I liked—and I trusted it. As a result my collection today is partly good, partly not so good. But for many reasons I am pleased with it. If some of the pictures that are less than great were once bought from friends I knew when we were young (many have since died), or are reminders of places I knew and loved, I cherish them no less than my Picassos, my Modiglianis, and my Rouaults.

The paintings I collected through the years are now scattered. Some hang on the walls of my apartments in London, New York, and Paris; others are in the Helena Rubinstein Pavilion of the museum in Tel Aviv, Israel. The mistakes are hidden away in cellars and cupboards. When I bought a picture because I thought I was getting a bargain, it most often turned out to be a mistake. But when I purchased what I knew gave me real inner joy, or because I wanted to encourage an artist whose talent I recognized, I usually chose well.

Much has been written and said about my collections of paintings, sculpture, African art, and opaline glass. To me they are simply part of my existence. I like to have them around me. Every piece has a personal memory, and now, in what Americans like to call my "senior citizen years," it is this sentimental value which overrides the fact that art has been an excellent investment for me.

Edward, too, had been busy during all this time with his own special interests, and during the twenties in Paris he launched an English literary magazine called *This Quarter*. Under the imprint of the Black Mannequin Press he also published many fine books, and he established an international reputation as one of the foremost translators of French, Polish, and Italian. He was perhaps best known in Paris for his publishing of the works of young American authors, and he was among the earliest editors in France

66

to acclaim publicly the brilliance of James Joyce, Ernest Hemingway, D. H. Lawrence, and E. E. Cummings, all of whom were his friends.

A passionate bibliophile, Edward at one time possessed the original manuscripts of *Ulysses* and *Lady Chatterley's Lover*. In fact, Lawrence was one of his favorite authors, and in 1929 he published a Paris edition of *Lady Chatterley's Lover*.

In the same year Lawrence surprised his admirers by making his debut as a painter, with an exhibition of his work which was arranged for him at the Warren Gallery in London. Most of the paintings were nudes, which shocked the conventional. There were many hostile critics, and the paintings were forcibly removed from the gallery by order of the Home Office. Lawrence was terribly hurt by this and he asked Edward to print his reply to the Home Secretary. It was a remarkable essay in his own defense and Edward was glad to publish it in *This Quarter*.

In contrast to his vital, vivid style of writing, D. H. Lawrence was taciturn and shy. In our home he would sit in a corner of the room refusing to mix with other guests. It was only when he noticed that I was as quiet and shy as he that he started talking to me. One evening it was I who did most of the talking. Edward had recently published, in unexpurgated form, Lawrence's short story "Sun." This had done much to encourage the cult of sun worshiping, and women began rushing off to the South of France to lie on the rocks and beaches. Most of them knew nothing of the dangers of prolonged sun-bathing. In spite of my efforts to teach them that it dried the moisture out of the skin, discoloring it and leaving lines and wrinkles behind, they insisted upon following the newest fad. I was very much against the sun cult. I still am. And I told Lawrence so.

"If I'd known," he said, "I would have scrapped the story or made it anti-sun."

Thoughts of Lawrence sadden me, for he seemed to be a young man tortured by his genius. One time he looked so ill that I begged him to borrow the Mill at Combs-la-Ville, our small country house about twenty-five miles outside Paris, and to stay there peacefully with his wife Frieda. But the wanderlust was too strong in him. He went off to the South of France and a few months later died at Vence. Edward was one of the few friends who attended Lawrence's funeral. He was buried in a small cemetery on the side of a mountain overlooking the Mediterranean. Over the grave stands a phoenix of his own design. It was carved out of local stone by a peasant who loved him and appreciated his kindness.

The American author William Faulkner was like Lawrence in many ways. He was quiet, aloof, and strangely removed from the life about him. The first time he came to our house his silence alarmed me. I thought he was ill. "No, ma'am," he assured me, "just thinking of home." Hemingway, on the other hand, was voluble and opinionated. Few men could have been more handsome and virile. He would talk at great length about himself and his successes with girls, but with a boyish charm. It was impossible not to like him.

James Joyce was down to earth. He loved lengthy discussions, particularly on the complexities of the written word. "Let me write your beauty advertisements," he suggested. "I'll use the style of *Ulysses* and women will be so puzzled they will rush out and buy. After all," he added cynically, "they only want to escape from themselves."

These were some of the men we knew in the twenties. Most of them are dead, but their names have not been forgotten. Of the women I knew and admired, Mademoiselle Chanel is one of the few to have grown in fame and stature during the years. Her age is her secret, but her energy, taste, and accomplishments have become a legend in her own lifetime. Chanel has always seemed to me the essence of chic, as a designer and as a woman. When I first knew her she had a small hat shop. In the early twenties she decided to enter the world of fashion. She was the first of the great designers to relate the clothes she designed to the women who wore them. Her basic idea was to make a woman look and feel young, and she designed "classic" clothes that were both beautiful and comfortable. Her innovations have been many. She introduced bobbed hair by cutting her own and startling the world. She popularized short skirts, horn-rimmed spectacles, backless shoes and trousers for women; and her No. 5 perfume has never lost its popularity. (No one had ever thought of a "dressmaker" perfume until Chanel launched one.)

Many years ago, during a dress fitting which she personally supervised, I asked Chanel why she had never married, especially since it was well known that a certain very rich English duke worshiped her.

"What? And become the third duchess?" she cried. "No. I am Mademoiselle Chanel and I shall remain so, just as you will always be Madame Rubinstein. These are our rightful titles."

And later, while talking of the great loves in her life, she gave me one of her sharp, knowing looks.

"Madame, you have never had a lover?"

I had to admit that I had had neither the time nor the inclination, to which she replied, "You may have been lucky." I wonder.

The years in Paris after World War I were successful ones for me. I was able to make frequent visits to all the countries in which I had salons, including America. My business was flourishing everywhere. But Edward was expressing more and more openly his disapproval of my constant rushing around and of my frequent absences from our home in Paris.

I did my best to allay his anxiety, but I failed to take his objections seriously. I thought he was merely being possessive. The growth and development of my business meant so much to me that I did not understand the extent of his unhappiness. Often his words would be tinged with real anger, which should have warned me. "You work too hard," he would say. "It's not necessary. I want you here at home, where you belong." But I was so completely caught up in the web of my work and planning that I considered the business my first duty. I realize what a failure I must have been at that time as a wife, even as a mother.

And then one day Edward told me that he had fallen in love with a younger woman. I was hurt and bewildered, but I could not absolve myself from all responsibility. Yet I desperately hoped that I could do something to win back Edward's affection.

Just at the time of this terrible crisis in my marriage, I was faced with another crisis in my business life. The New York firm of Wall Street bankers, Lehman Brothers, offered me several million dollars for the American business. They promised, too, that every one of my staff would be kept on. I had received offers before, but none so tempting or so well timed. If I could free myself of the American business, I thought, my life could be lived happily in Paris, by Edward's side. Our marriage might yet be saved.

My decision was a quick one. I accepted Lehman Brothers' offer and hastily set sail for America, in order to sign the papers.

Many stories of this "take-over" have been circulated and many explanations given. It has been described as a brilliant financial deal, an example of "genius timing." But there was nothing especially clever about it. I sold the American corporation for one reason only—to save my marriage. It was a sacrifice, for my business had always meant more to me than money. Besides, every instinct told me that bankers would have neither the training nor the intuition necessary to operate a cosmetic company. I felt there was no alternative, however.

My stay in America was brief, only long enough to complete the transaction. The return trip to Paris seemed endlessly long. One day I felt elated; the next day I would be filled with doubts. When finally I arrived home, Edward told me that he had made up his mind. He was determined that we must separate.

It was a case of the two saddest words in any marital breakup—"too late." And I had no one to blame but myself.

I was numb. There was no fight left in me as I heard Edward say, "Nothing will ever change you, Helena. Your business is your life."

As it turned out, the same circumstances that had helped to wreck my marriage had their salutary effect in another direction. During my instructional tours of the department stores in the States, I had made many friends among the store owners and they kept in frequent touch with me. As time went on they complained bitterly of the way in which the American business was being run by the new owners. Some wrote regretfully that it would no longer be possible for them to sell the Rubinstein preparations. Distribution had been expanded and the new sales methods had vulgarized my products.

These distress signals helped to take my mind off my personal troubles, at least to some degree. Without publicizing the fact, I began to buy back some of the stock on the open market, until eventually I held one-third of it. Then as a substantial shareholder I wrote to Lehman Brothers, registering a strong complaint. For a while they ignored me, while the business diminished and the stock continued to fall in price. Unable to restrain myself, I circulated a letter to all of the stockholders, informing them that I felt the Rubinstein business was being jeopardized and urging them to add their complaints to mine.

Then came the Wall Street crash. Millions of dollars were lost overnight, and people were frantic. The value of the Rubinstein stock fell from sixty to three dollars per share. By that time Lehman Brothers were anxious to get it off their hands at any cost, and I bought back the controlling interest in the business for a fraction of what they had paid me. I desperately needed an interest which would keep me occupied so that I would have no time to think of anything else; besides, I knew in my heart that no one else could run the business as I could. Both the cosmetic and fashion businesses, I have learned over the years, are best run as personal enterprises.

Ahead of me once more was the lonely treadmill of work . . . never had I felt so utterly alone.

6 ∮ Years of Change

IF I hoped to save the American business, it would be necessary for me to make the long, dreary trip back to the States again. I could scarcely bear the thought. I was struggling to hide my feelings over the collapse of my marriage, and at the same time I dreaded to think how divorce might affect the lives of my two sons. I wanted them close to me. Their laughter, even their occasional teen-age squabbles, gave me pleasure. The very sound of their voices helped to distract me from my own thoughts.

It would be less dreadful for us all, I thought, if I were to take the boys with me to the States; and they were delighted with the prospect. Roy, in particular, expressed an early interest in the business. To keep them occupied during the first few months after our arrival in America, I suggested that they might be interested in learning something about the American factory and how the Rubinstein products were manufactured. To my great surprise they thought it an excellent idea, and thereafter they continued to work in the factory during their summer vacations. Horace was less enthusiastic than Roy, but he went along with my proposal. Horace, like Edward and my own father, was the artistic one. Like them, he preferred books to bookkeeping.

For a long time work was my only consolation. I drove myself relentlessly, just as I had during those first years in Melbourne. I made no concession to the fact that I was now a middle-aged woman, and very soon I was on the verge of a breakdown. Sleepless nights followed one another for months. Daily I grew more tense and more difficult to work with. I prefer not to think what my poor staff had to put up with in those days.

Then came the news of my father's death. I had loved my father dearly, but I was by now so deeply involved in the business, and there were so many people depending on me for their livelihood, that I felt it was impossible for me to drop everything in order to attend the funeral. Manka, who could more easily be spared, left for Poland immediately, to be with Mama. Her trip took more than a week, and by the time Manka arrived in Cracow, my mother, too, was dead.

I could not shake off the despondency that settled on me when the news reached me. I blamed myself bitterly for having been so engrossed in my own affairs that I really believed it impossible to make that one last trip to Cracow while my mother was still alive. I should have made it possible at any cost. For weeks I brooded until a good friend, who was also a physician, gave me some invaluable advice.

"What is the sense of building a business if you kill yourself in the effort?" he asked. "If you were anyone else I would prescribe a long sea voyage, but you would never allow yourself the time. Very well, you have always told me that you like to be the first to try anything new. Diet is just beginning to be recognized as playing an important part in mental and physical fitness. Why don't you go to the new Bircher-Benner Sanatorium in Zurich and learn about their treatment and their diets? It will take your mind away from the business, which will run perfectly well without you for a while, and you will more than make up for any lost time once you are feeling fit again."

I accepted the challenge and set out for Switzerland and the Bircher-Benner clinic—not very hopefully, although I was interested in their new theories on diet; but I felt so wretched, I was prepared to try anything. Within the first few days I knew I had come to the right place. In fact, I regard my meeting with Dr. Bircher-Benner, pioneer of the science of dietetics, as one of the outstanding events of my life. Many of the ideas he fought for are accepted today as a matter of course, but long before any of his contemporaries he recognized the value of vitamins, the vital influence of nutrition on health, and the supreme importance of fresh foods of all kinds.

There is, of course, no food which by itself will work a miracle; but a wide and varied combination of the right kinds of foods, grown in the right way, will do much to help produce a healthy body, a sound mind, good nerves, and vigorous energy. For three weeks I lived on a diet of Muesli (a mixture of rolled oats, lemon juice, sweetened condensed milk, grated apples, and hazelnuts) and plenty of other raw fruits and vegetables. As my tensions lessened I began to sleep well, and in fifteen days I lost ten pounds. As I regained my vitality my mind was once more filled with plans for the future.

After the prescribed three weeks I returned to Paris. Everyone was astonished at the change in my appearance —and in my mood! I could barely wait to get back to New York, where I was eager to adapt all I had learned at Bircher-Benner to the American way of life. Not everyone could afford the time and money to visit Switzerland; the least I could do was to pass on the knowledge I had acquired there.

"Come for a Day of Beauty," our new American advertisements read. "Slimming low-calorie lunches . . . massage . . . relaxing facials."

"A Day of Beauty" at the Helena Rubinstein salons became a major attraction for women all over the world. In one eight-hour day clients were "done over" from head to foot. The morning hours were spent in measuring, weighing, and charting the individual needs of each client, followed by corrective exercises under the supervision of an attending physician. A shower and body massage were next on the agenda, after which came a carefully planned, low-calorie luncheon and a fifteen-minute rest period. In the afternoon the client was put into the hands of a capable beauty operator, her hair shampooed, cut, and set in

75

the latest, most flattering fashion, and her hands and feet were manicured. The last hour was spent in a make-up lesson given by one of our beauty experts. By the end of the day the client looked and felt like a new woman, not only in appearance but in spirit, "so much lighter, and more fit," was the favorite way of expressing it.

The low-calorie lunches, unfortunately, were not a financial success.

Others copied the idea more successfully a few years later, but apparently my original project had been premature. Besides, I lacked experience in the running of a restaurant. We lost a good deal of money on this portion of the venture, but in every other way the "Day of Beauty" was a huge success, and it has remained so ever since under Mala's guidance.

Since my separation from Edward I had refused innumerable invitations. It was impossible for me to pretend to be lighthearted. I preferred to lose myself in my work. But in 1935, on one of my frequent business trips to Paris, I was invited to dinner in the home of the Comtesse de Polignac, the daughter of Jeanne Lanvin whose famous dress house was very near my salon in the Faubourg. I accepted her invitation. After dinner we played bridge, and my partner that evening was a charming Georgian whose full name was Prince Artchil Gourielli-Tchkonia. He was a big, handsome, curly-headed man with a contagious laugh. I liked his frankness and his warmth as much as his gaiety. Not in a very long time had I enjoyed an evening so much.

During the next few weeks we met frequently at the houses of mutual friends, and one day I invited Artchil for bridge, at my apartment on the Ile St. Louis, Quai de Bethune.

I had bought this property in 1930 when I was Edward's wife, with a view to rebuilding. Situated on a quiet street overlooking the Seine, it lies almost in the shadow of the Cathedral of Notre Dame. It had taken me five years to persuade the existing tenants to move from the old dilapidated building, but eventually a new apartment house was constructed in its place by the brilliant French architect Louis Sue. The top floor afforded a magnificent view of Paris, which I loved, and this was the floor I selected for my home. Sue had also designed a delightful roof garden which extended the entire length and breadth of the building, encompassing the skyline of Paris from the Sacré Coeur to the Panthéon.

Some of my friends have described the apartment as having the "most expensive view in Paris." But what pleases me is that the terrace is one of the loveliest spots in the world. From a huge fountain, water cascades from one wide, deep blue basin to another, surrounded by flower beds filled with seasonal plantings and evergreens. In one corner there is a dining arbor, shielded from the wind by high glass panels and climbing vines. Here Artchil and I dined the night he first came to dinner.

After dinner we played bridge and, as was to become usual, Artchil won. He teased me about my conservative game. "You don't hesitate to gamble a fortune on a beauty formula," he cheerfully exclaimed, "but you hate yourself for losing a few points at bridge."

As we said good night, Artchil asked me when I could dine with him. Ruefully I reminded him that I would be sailing for New York the following morning.

"That's all right," he answered, unperturbed. "Where do you like to dine in New York?"

"At the Colony," I told him, smiling, never suspecting that he meant it seriously. Two weeks later he telephoned me, in New York. He had just arrived and he meant to hold me to my promise, he said. Within an hour he called for me at my home, and that evening we dined at the Colony.

How could I resist such a man? Our courtship was brief. In his usual direct way he said, "We are neither of us children, Helena, and you need me."

Always before I had been told that people needed me. It had not occurred to me that I, too, needed some one person to share my hectic and exhausting life and give me the comfort of constant companionship. I did need him; I needed his laughter, his affection, and the devotion he gave so generously. I hesitated only because I was a few years older than he, but our mutual friends and my family finally convinced me. Even the boys were enthusiastic.

We were married in 1938, and for the next twenty years our life together was one of contentment and mutual

77

esteem. Artchil became genuinely interested in the business and helped me a great deal. Moreover, he was a kindly, considerate man, and I could relax with him more easily than with anyone I had ever known. When he felt I was becoming too engrossed in business he would mention, casually, that he had heard of a dealer with an interesting collection of antiques or china, or he might tell me of some promising young artist he had met. It was a challenge I could never resist, and he knew it. We were seldom apart; in fact, we were separated only when we had to travel long distances. Artchil hated traveling by plane, so if I had to fly to attend an urgent conference, he would follow more slowly, by train or by boat.

We planned to live in New York during the winters and in Europe during spring and summer, spending the Paris season at the Quai de Bethune apartment which we both loved. But alas for our plans! We were in Paris in 1939 when, for the second time in my life, war was declared between Germany and France. Hoping against hope, we stayed on until after the German break-through, when it became imperative for us to flee, leaving behind our apartment in Paris and the Mill. All of our cherished possessions, not to mention the entire French business, were left to the mercy of the invaders.

Even so, we very nearly stayed on too long. At the last moment we were barely able to get passage on what turned out to be the final sailing of the SS *Manhattan*. But we were fortunate to have escaped at all, more fortunate than many of our friends. Fourteen days later we landed in New York.

The years of World War II were endless, terrible years. Although we were in America, with none of the hardships so many in Europe were suffering, I sometimes think our mental anguish was almost as great. We lived from day to day, always waiting for the postman and the longed-for news of family and friends.

Paris was in the hands of the Nazis. My London salon in Grafton Street had been bombed, but mercifully no one there had been hurt. After some months, however, the news reached us that my sister Regina had been killed by the Germans. And with all this heartbreak there were separations at home no less difficult. Roy joined the Army;

78

Horace, too, volunteered. My nephew Oscar Kolin was with the French Army. He had been captured by the Nazis at the time of the evacuation of Dunkirk, but had miraculously managed to escape. Later he worked with the Underground movement in France.

Fortunately my sister Ceska was able eventually to come to New York after several harrowing months in the London blitz, and when the war was finally ended my nephew Oscar joined us, with his wife and children. I was grateful, too, that my first two grandchildren were with me, Toby and her young brother Barry, both Horace's children. For some years I had great hopes that one or both of these grandchildren would take an interest in the business. I would have liked to think that it would continue under the direction of members of my family for the next three hundred years at least. But the artistic strain seems to have come out more strongly in them than the "merchant" strain. Today Toby is painting and Barry is a promising writer. As for my third grandchild, Roy's little daughter, Helena, she is still too young to know in which direction her talents will develop, but I continue to hope.

The best antidote to worry, I have always believed, is work and more work; hence during every spare moment in the war years I kept our research laboratories going at full pressure. If anyone suggested that my business was an unnecessary luxury in wartime, there was a sharp reply from me. I feel that it is in periods of trouble and depression that women really need the color and the uplift of make-up, the reassurance of helpful treatment, the joy and escape of fragrance. On a visit to the White House around this time I asked President Roosevelt what I could do to be of help to the war effort. He had just been reading a London newspaper, he told me, and he was much impressed with the story of a woman who was carried out of a blitzed building on a stretcher. Before she would agree to take a sedative she pleaded with the ambulance attendant to find her lipstick and give it to her. "It does something for me," she said. "Your war effort," President Roosevelt assured me, "is to help keep up the morale of our women. And you are doing it splendidly."

During the war years we worked, we hoped, we prayed that soon there would be an end to the horror that was taking the lives of so many young men. At last there came victory, first in Europe and later in Japan. Even those who had suffered the greatest tragedies were able to share in the general rejoicing that, for the time being, made the whole civilized world one.

On V-J Day I telephoned every travel office in New York, begging them to find a place for me on the first available plane, passenger boat or freighter leaving for Europe. Ten days later I was aboard a Liberty ship bound for France. I could get only one reservation, sharing a cabin with five other women. Artchil agreed that he would follow on the next available boat.

I shall never forget my first sight of Paris. It broke my heart. Before doing anything else, I asked those members of my old staff with whom I could get in touch for news of friends and fellow workers. I also made inquiries through the police, and with such addresses and information as we could obtain, a group of us set out on a daily search, meeting in the evenings to compare notes and to make our plans for the next day. Some of my dearest friends I never saw or heard from again. Others whom I found had lost everything. I was thankful that the majority were still alive and, although invariably half-starved, comparatively well and cheerful.

My apartment at Quai de Bethune became a meeting place and canteen. It had been occupied by the Germans and left tragically ransacked and abused. Precious pieces of sculpture had obviously been used for target practice. A lovely Greek statue of Aphrodite was riddled with bullet holes, and I keep it in the entrance hall to this day, as a reminder of the senseless destruction of war. A good deal of the furniture was missing and a lot more severely damaged. My exquisite Louis XVI card tables had been set out on the terrace and left there through the winter months, in the rain and the snow. But what upset me the most was to learn that much of the furniture had been hurled out of the windows just before the Nazis vacated the building, in one final, senseless act of destruction. It was an extraordinary thing for grown men to do. Even more extraordinary was to find the nineteenth-century carpet in the main salon perforated with thousands of neat circular holes. The design of the carpet, on which a master

80

craftsman had worked so lovingly and painstakingly, had apparently made a splendid target for revolver practice. In spite of the damage, however, the apartment was still habitable. At least there were a number of beds and some bed linen, and we were thankful to be able to camp there. Material possessions had little or no value at the time.

The Mill at Combs-la-Ville was in worse condition. It was an empty shell. The furniture had vanished, and every bathtub, hand basin, and lavatory bowl had been smashed.

The most important thing at hand, however, was to concentrate on getting the business in the Faubourg St. Honoré in some sort of working order, so that I might have jobs to offer to those of my old staff who were still alive and who wanted to come back. The salon had been operated by the Germans for a time, then closed for lack of merchandise. But before I was allowed to take possession again, I had to prove my ownership. This meant endless forms to be signed and interminable interviews, but eventually all was settled. Then began the search for small quantities of essential oils and other ingredients so that I could get busy in my "kitchen." At the same time I found what builders and decorators I could and set them to work on the more pressing jobs. All this took weeks to accomplish, while I waited impatiently for Artchil's arrival from the States. I had written to him earlier, asking him to arrange for shipment of those items which we needed most desperately, but shortages of materials and transport delays made progress slow. Months passed before we could really set to work again, but gradually we did get started.

Fortunately my son Horace was able to join me. We had no car and we could not have had any gasoline for it if we had had one. Horace and I walked the three miles to and from the business each day, since it was often impossible to get on the Metro; but the exercise was good for us both, we decided, and we came to enjoy our daily walks. We were glad to be alive and busy, and there was no time for looking back or for vain regrets.

Artchil finally did arrive. Transatlantic passenger service had had to be kept to a minimum those first few months after the war, with "top priority" people given first preference. Only because of a last-minute cancellation had he been able to get a reservation at all. When I saw Artchil again I realized more than ever how much I needed his calm, reassuring presence and his smiling, gentle ways.

In time I was able to get over to London for a few days, to see how things were going there. Since the bombing in Grafton Street we had acquired temporary offices in Berkeley Square, but they were much too small for our needs. As I started on the search for larger quarters, with Artchil by my side, and with half a dozen real estate agents all eager to be of service, I could not help thinking of another search years before, when I had been a stranger to London, with no one to help me. By now I knew every corner of that great city, but during those early years even the names of the streets had bewildered me, St. James's, Park Lane, South Audley Street. And I could still recall my poor tired feet at the end of the long days of walking.

How many worlds had been overturned since then, and how many young lives lost!

By an incredible stroke of luck I managed to find just what I wanted—a long lease on No. 3 Grafton Street, near our original premises, and one of London's loveliest eighteenth-century houses. Through its doors had walked many of the most famous beauties of the past, and it was here, too, that Mrs. Willie James, last of the great Edwardian hostesses, had entertained King Edward VII. It was the perfect spot for a beauty salon, and it continues to be our London headquarters. The magnificent staircase and the second floor balcony are as lovely today as when I first saw the building. To have altered or changed either of them would have been sacrilege.

It was in the late 1940s, on our return from Europe, that Artchil and I embarked on a new American venture. It was high time, said Artchil, that we did something for men, and I agreed. The American man with his crew-cut hair, his uniform white shirt and dark suit, seemed to us much too standardized. The British were showing far greater individuality. Sir Winston Churchill sported a jaunty bow tie and square bowler to accentuate the resolute lines of his jaw; Prime Minister-to-be Harold Macmillan dressed with studied Edwardian carelessness; and the elegant Rex Harrison, just then emerged as a popular cinema star, affected extravagantly patterned tweed coats with matching tweed hats and cardigans.

They were men of conviction, who wore what pleased them, and they selected their wardrobes down to the smallest detail with confidence and instinctive good taste. These trends were being copied by many men in England who were conscious of the importance of their appearance.

For our new American venture we found a small town house close to the St. Regis Hotel in New York and there, using Artchil's family name, we opened "The House of Gourielli for Men." On the street floor a *boutique* sold imported English and Italian pullovers, ties, socks, and other accessories dear to the masculine heart. In the barbershop on the floor above we introduced such novelties as fresh tangy colognes made especially for men, hair tinting, and the fitting of toupees (strictly confidential, of course). There were private cubicles for facials and a special oxygen machine to give a man a quick "pickup" after a late night. Arrangements were also made with a nearby restaurant to serve "gourmet" luncheons, and we had ticker tapes installed so that businessmen could keep in touch with the latest Wall Street quotations while away from their offices.

The House of Gourielli became "the place" among a select circle, and many a famous name was listed among the regular clientele. One story put around New York was that the cinema star, Yul Brynner, came to East Fifty-fifth Street especially to have his head shaved and polished! As a matter of fact, it was his shoes that were polished by our doorman and bootblack extraordinary. Gleaming chauffeur-driven limousines arrived at the front door at all hours of the day, and Lou would be whisked away to shine the imported shoes of one celebrity or another, we thought—until one day we learned that his unusual popularity was due not so much to his remarkable talent as a bootblack but because he was a bookmaker! That, regretfully, was the last we saw of him.

The clientele of the House of Gourielli remained a little too select, however. Once again we realized that we had been in advance of the times. Nevertheless, I predict that before much longer men will be using almost as many toilet preparations as women do. Already the trend is under way. Masculine fragrances in aftershave lotions and skin bracers are accepted everywhere, and many men have their favorite colognes. Wigs and hair pieces, cleverly fitted, give added assurance to innumerable men, and hair coloring is used increasingly to darken gray hair. I heartily approve, because I believe that a man's appearance is one of his greatest assets.

The years following the last war, with their restrictions and shortages, gave rise to many fads and experiments in the field of beauty—not all of them successful. One of these was royal jelly. For a time it made front-page news and caused a small upheaval even in the thinking of so-called beauty experts. All sorts of miraculous healing and rejuvenating properties were claimed for it, and it was introduced into innumerable beauty preparations. Some years earlier one of my French chemists had been engaged in research on royal jelly. He had reported that although the queen bee's nourishment contained certain rejuvenating powers indispensable in prolonging the life of the queen bee, it could never be extracted in sufficient quantities to be used as an effective beauty aid for women.

When I saw the claims that were suddenly being made in many countries for royal jelly, I determined to do a little research of my own. I flew to New Zealand to consult with Sir Edmund Hillary, the world's greatest apiarist (and the first man to reach the top of Mount Everest). I asked Sir Edmund to tell me what he knew about royal jelly and its potential as an ingredient in beauty preparations. I can still hear his voice as he said, with the authority of his lifetime of experience, "By all means, eat honey, Madame. You will derive much energy from it. But forget the myth of its rejuvenating or beautifying purposes. That's strictly for the bees. Not all the apiarists in New Zealand could produce more than a few pounds of royal jelly in a year, and you would need tons of it to supply a mass market with an effective cream."

Sir Edmund's words closed the subject, as far as I was concerned. How glad I am that we never introduced this ingredient into any of our preparations. Time and experience have proved how ineffective it was. Within a few short months royal jelly disappeared from the market as suddenly as it had appeared.

Perhaps I am a heretic to say this, but despite the fact that I am constantly searching for new, helpful ideas for Helena Rubinstein products, I believe there are far too many "gimmicks" in beauty care today. I am aware that many of the younger women and girls who represent a large part of the market buy these gadgets for "fun," for an exciting change, for the lift that can often make a woman feel more beautiful. But beauty is much more than a "gimmick." Its essence is constant care and discipline. I still use essentially the same cream that I took from Poland to Australia and later modified and sold under my own name. I still do as many calisthenics as I can, either in my bathtub or in bed. I still prefer not to smoke, and I drink lightly if at all. At the same time I wish that all women paid greater attention to their natural radiance, resulting from physical exercise, proper diet and, above all, from inner serenity. All the eye make-up on the market cannot illuminate eyes that have lost their interest in the world, and a woman in love with life has the best basic "foundation" to be found anywhere.

7   Beautiful Things

MANY times I have been asked why I keep several homes open all year round, in different parts of the world, and how I manage to do it. I don't like asking friends to visit me in a hotel; it is too impersonal. I like to receive them in my own surroundings. My secret for running this complicated network of houses (sometimes referred to behind my back, I have been told, as the "Rubinstein Hiltons") is to have a married couple in residence in each one. And I am rather proud of the fact that each couple has been with me for an average of thirty-five years. Eugenie in Paris has been with me for over forty years; Annette at Combs-la-Ville was at the Mill when I bought it in the early 1930s; and the couple who look after my home in Greenwich, Connecticut, Leo and Margaret Bergeron, have been there since Edward and I bought the house in 1915. In New York, Albert, my faithful Filipino butler, has helped to run the apartment for the last twenty-three years.

Because my homes have been written about and photographed so often, and because they are filled with antique furniture and works of art, it does not mean that they are stuffy, unlived-in places. The first requisite of a home, to me, is that it should be comfortable; and wherever I am I insist that my rooms be filled with flowers so as to emanate a lived-in, homey atmosphere. I am forever changing the furniture around, keeping the rooms "alive" with new curtains, new covers, fresh paint. And every few months the paintings and African primitives which I love are shifted from one room to another.

My seemingly unconventional taste has been frequently commented upon. The explanation is simple, really: I like many different kinds of beautiful things and I am not afraid to use them in untraditional ways. One or two rooms in each house are kept for storage purposes, and I like nothing better than spending a rainy Saturday or Sunday rummaging around in them for an old vase, a picture, or a long forgotten *bibelot*. This is how I have rediscovered many a treasured object which I had almost forgotten existed.

My principal home, where I spend six months of the year, and where I now write, is in New York. It was during World War II that I began making plans for this three-story apartment on Park Avenue, fourteen floors up. "I have fallen in love with a castle in the air," I wrote to my son Roy. This is what it seemed to me at first sight, although I was told repeatedly that I was mad even to consider it; it was much too large and would be difficult to run. Not only did I consider it, I bought the whole building. Through the years the penthouse apartment at 625 Park Avenue has become my favorite home and the meeting place of all the members of my large family. Every room has its happy memories. Roy and his wife, Niuta, live only a few blocks away, as do my nephew, Oscar Kolin, and his family; and my relatives in all branches of the business in many countries know that my house in New York is open to them whenever they visit here. I enjoy having my family stay with me. At Christmas time especially we have a family get-together, a somewhat unorthodox dinner starting with Polish hors d'oeuvres, *piroshki* and caviar, going on to turkey, Christmas pudding, and mince pies.

I am happy, too, to lend the apartment in New York when it can serve a useful purpose, such as for charitable causes to which I contribute. It is used for all kinds of business activities, and I keep one room solely for conferences. I call it the "chintz room" because it resembles so many of the rooms in our first American home in Greenwich. Roy often teases me about it. "You keep it that way purposely," he says, "to remind me of Greenwich. You know I can't disagree with you in such surroundings—the past is too strong!"

The Park Avenue apartment had originally been built by a banker who had a large family. After his death the family tried in vain to let the place, but because of its size, twenty-six rooms and eight bathrooms, it remained empty for six and a half years until I came along. Even my estate agents looked on it as a "white elephant." They insisted that it could not be run without the help of a huge staff. Nevertheless an efficient staff of only three people, who live in, look after the apartment and my personal needs, with extra help to do the heavy cleaning and to lend a hand when I am entertaining. This is the modern American way, and I consider it extremely sensible.

The sun, when it shines, pours into the apartment, and I might be living in the country, since on the main floor there is a terrace planted with evergreens, flowering borders, and several weeping willows. Over the years, with a few changes, the terrace has taken on at different times the look of an English rose garden, of an herb garden, a Japanese rockery, and once, for a particular party, a reasonable facsimile of a Hawaiian jungle, with orchids trailing over a specially constructed waterfall.

During the worst of the war years the terrace of our New York apartment was turned into our "farm in the sky," and we grew a good many of our own vegetables. And once when the apartment was thrown open to the City Gardens Club, to help raise funds for city children who yearned for a garden of their own, all the colors of the field and the hothouses appeared in flowering plants, the full length of the terrace.

One room on the entrance floor of the apartment has been made into a cardroom for my favorite game of bridge. In 1942 I asked Salvador Dali to paint murals for three of the walls of this room. In his surrealistic style he

89

produced three huge panels depicting with great restraint and elegance Morning, Noon, and Night. I remember the evening when the panels were first shown. One of my guests asked the artist whether they had any hidden meaning. "The whole thing is an allegory of life," Dali explained. "It is for the viewer to decipher. If no meaning is found, then there is none."

When the murals were finished, Dali with his restless imagination suggested turning our cardroom into a music room. "I will design a fountain spouting from a grand piano. It will hang from the ceiling and never be played. That," he added, "is the essence of surrealism."

But fortunately Dali was soon busy elsewhere, and I was able to furnish the room as I had intended, as a cardroom with eighteenth-century baroque furniture and sensible tables to play on. I may be a bit unconventional, but I am also practical.

In the corridor leading to the cardroom are the master bedrooms, much too large by modern standards, each about forty feet long and each with an adjoining bathroom of similar proportions. My own bathroom, I confess, is also too large for me, but I have had cupboards installed along one wall, to hold linen and clothes, so that it serves a double purpose. I hate wasted space.

In the last year or two my bedroom has become a place where I hold many business meetings, since the doctors insist that I must remain in bed several mornings each week. The room is large enough to hold a dozen people comfortably, and it is furnished with the transparent lucite furniture which a dear friend, Ladislas Medgyes, designed for me when I first moved in. I am still a trifle overwhelmed by the bed, which lights up head and foot; but I must admit that beautiful, unusual beds have always held a fascination for me. In London I have an intricately carved Portuguese oak bed which dates from the sixteenth century. It was discovered in a small antique shop near Estoril, and it cost only $160.

In Paris I have a bed which was originally made for the Empress Eugénie, wife of Napoleon III. Encrusted with mother-of-pearl, it has matching side tables and chairs. Artchil hated this furniture when we were first married. He claimed that it looked too opulent. I once had a great

90

row with him when I caught him deliberately chipping the mother-of-pearl. He defended himself by insisting, "I was only trying to give it a lived-in look."

Hung on the walls of all three floors in the New York apartment are some of the paintings I have collected over the years. At one time I was an enthusiastic collector of Renoirs. I had known him and admired his work, which had great feeling as well as a subtle delicacy. The man himself was a delightful person with kindly, laughing eyes. When we first met, before World War I, art dealers were already competing for his paintings, but he accepted their tribute with a large grain of salt. "Me a genius?" he would say. "What nonsense! Once an artist thinks he has genius, he's done for. The only salvation is to work like a laborer and have no delusions of grandeur."

The very first time Renoir and I met he was in a huff. He had just been offered 50,000 francs for one of his portraits. "It is much too much," he fumed. "No living artist should be paid such a sum!" I wish that I had a portrait of myself, painted by Renoir. Many well-known artists have painted me, sometimes out of pure interest in me as a model, sometimes because I felt I could help them. Salvador Dali claims that he was recognized as a portrait painter in America only after he painted my portrait. And Elie Nadelman was launched in this country when I arranged for his first private showing. Lincoln Kirstein, in the Museum of Modern Art's publication on Nadelman, has described my first meeting with this talented man in London in 1911:

"Into the Paterson Gallery walked a compatriot of Nadelman's, Madame Helena Rubinstein, later Princess Gourielli, a sympathetic collector. She did not acquire merely one or two heads; she purchased the entire exhibition outright. Her patronage of Nadelman, coming when it did, was the most influential of his career. Madame Rubinstein mounted his pieces in her handsome establishments in London, Paris, and New York; a symbol of the scientific beautification of modern woman . . ."

The two words in Kirstein's paragraph which touch me especially are "sympathetic collector." I was indeed sympathetic to Nadelman's work. He had great charm; he was a fellow Pole, and he expressed in his art what I was trying to say in my advertising to women all over the world. To me, Nadelman's purity of line and his feeling for form say "beauty" better than all the fancy words coined for the beauty industry by Madison Avenue. Yet I suppose both are necessary.

Having one's portrait painted is something of a gamble. I realize that an artist must be free to interpret what he sees in his own way; but there are times when I look at some of the portraits that have been done of me and I comfort myself with the words of Sargent: "A portrait is a likeness with something slightly wrong about the mouth."

The French woman painter, Marie Laurencin, painted me looking like an Indian maharanee. Raoul Dufy produced a breezy water color in which I appear dressed in red, white, and blue, as if draped in a flag. Tchelitchew, the romantic Russian painter, saw me as a sad-eyed young woman—then, as an afterthought, he sprinkled multi-colored sequins over the face. In the portrait by Dali I stand chained by ropes of emeralds to a high rock. He felt that I was bound by my possessions, which is very far from the truth. It was Bérard who, knowing of my love for children, painted my favorite portrait in a simple white smock with a shawl on my shoulders, my arm around a dark-haired young boy—my son Horace.

The last portrait of me, done by Graham Sutherland, portrays me as an eagle-eyed matriarch! At first I hated it, but with time the picture has grown on me. And I remind myself that some art critics have likened it to a Renaissance masterpiece. Sutherland himself chose the dress, an embroidered red evening gown from Balenciaga. He made endless sketches and many studies before he would even set to work on the final canvas. After a number of sittings I had to return to the States, but before he left London for his home in Kent where he finished the portrait, Sutherland snipped a bit of fabric from the hem of the dress to carry away with him, to be sure of reproducing the color and texture accurately. I heard nothing from him for six months. On one of my brief visits to London I received a message from Mr. Sutherland saying that I could see the finished portrait at a small frame maker's in the King's Road, Chelsea. When I got there I found not one but two life-size portraits of myself! I was at a loss for words, because neither of them really pleased me. They were both incredibly bold, domineering interpretations of what I had never imagined I looked like. I had never seen myself in such a harsh light. Yet later, when they were exhibited at the Tate Gallery, although I scarcely recognized myself through Sutherland's eyes, I had to admit that as paintings they were indeed masterpieces. With their brilliant color and marvelous brushwork, they nearly overpowered everything else in the Tate. One of the portraits was purchased by Lord Beaverbrook for his gallery in Fredericton, Canada. The other hangs in the entrance hallway of my New York apartment. Whenever I have a moment to study it I wonder : . . . am I really the austere, determined woman Sutherland painted so masterfully?

Will there be still another shock in store for me when I finally see Picasso's finished portrait of me? Picasso has been a friend for over forty years. I first met him at one of his early exhibitions in Paris, where I fell in love with a small oil painting of his, of a very young boy. I bought it, and Picasso came over to tell me that the painting was of his son, young Pablo, which pleased me very much. I have since collected quite a number of his paintings as well as the famous tapestry, "Women," which hangs in my living room in New York.

More than ten years ago, when I visited Picasso at his villa outside Cannes, he started a portrait of me. He must have done at least fifty sketches, from the waist to the level of my eyes—but he never completed the head. I sat for those sketches in a makeshift dining room from which I could look out over the tangled jungle of a garden scattered with his marvelous bronzes, to the Mediterranean beyond. I wore a brightly colored Mexican blouse which he had selected for me, and I sat very still as he sharpened his pencils. He hummed a little tune. Suddenly he said, "I am going to take a few notes, Helena . . . like a policeman!" He drew swiftly, giving little grunts of satisfaction as his pencil flew over the paper while he questioned me.

"First, how old are you?" he asked.

"Older than you," I replied, and this seemed to delight him. He then looked at me long and carefully.

"You have large ears," he said. "They are as large as

93

mine. Elephants also have large ears. They live forever. We will too!" Then he put down his pencil and looked at me still more closely.

"The distance between your ears and your eyes is exactly the same as mine," he shouted gleefully.

"What does that mean?"

"It means you are a genius—just like me!"

But the portrait has never been finished. Whenever I see Picasso I ask the same question: "When are you going to finish that painting of me?" And each time I receive the same reply: "What's the hurry? You and I have many years yet. There is plenty of time."

I recall another painter, a Mexican, whom I met some years ago and have never forgotten. It was Christmas time and Artchil had persuaded me to go to Mexico with him. We planned to take the thermal baths there and to have a real rest. We arrived in Mexico City, but before reaching the spa I noticed some colorful Mexican shawls in one of the shops near our hotel. A young man stood behind a counter wrapping parcels in tissue paper—but such tissue paper as I had never seen before. It was hand-painted with beautifully worked, stylized figures. I asked where it had been purchased and whether I could buy a few sheets. The young man explained that he was an artist, but too poor to buy canvas or paper, so he painted on the tissue paper which was later used for wrapping packages. He gladly offered me as much of the tissue as I could carry away. I became interested in this unusual young man. His name was Jesus Reyes, he told me. Instead of taking the thermal baths, we asked Jesus Reyes if he would be our guide, and through his eyes we saw Mexico as we had never seen any country before. Later I was able to arrange a showing of his tissue-paper paintings. It was a great success and enabled him to buy canvas, paint, and paper enough to last him the rest of his life. He has since become quite well known throughout Mexico and South America.

From Mexico, Artchil and I traveled to Brazil and from there to Argentina, where the lovely, progressive city of Buenos Aires appealed to me so that I decided it was the perfect center for our South American business operations. At first I was told it was impossible, there was no suitable building for sale. But exploring the city by myself, which is something I always enjoy, I found exactly the street I liked. I followed the suggestion of friends and instructed a firm of local lawyers to approach the owners of several of the houses on this street. Perhaps someone would be willing to sell? On the following Monday the lawyers opened negotiations, and by Wednesday evening two of the houses were mine. Only slight structural alterations were necessary, and a month later our first South American salon was opened to the public.

Another time, when Artchil and I were in Rome, we met so many talented but impoverished young Italian artists that on the spur of the moment we decided to organize an exhibition of their work. None of them had ever been to America, and we proposed that twenty of them paint their imaginary interpretations of the United States. The results were fascinating. Aldo Pagliacci, who painted burning churches, depicted St. Patrick's Cathedral on fire. Nino Caffe, whose penchant was for the Church, painted priests playing baseball. Colombotto Rosso's selection was of the Rocky Mountains rising out of the sea, and Leonardo Cremonini did an abstract which he entitled "Nebraska." Before the paintings were shipped to America, they were exhibited at L'Obelisco Gallery in Rome, and they have since been seen in many parts of the United States and in South America.

It was this venture which later led me to found the Helena Rubinstein Traveling Art Scholarship, awarded each year to an aspiring Australian artist, in memory of what that country had helped me to achieve.

Although Artchil and I usually agreed in our taste for painting, we would sometimes have small rows about the clothes I wore.

"Wear your black, Helena, with diamonds and a sable coat," he once said in his slightly dictatorial Russian way.

"But diamonds are cold," I objected, "and furs are too hot. *And* I've just bought the most wonderful gown in brilliant emerald brocade, embroidered with gold thread and pearls!" He was furious until he saw the dress on me. Then he gallantly agreed with my choice.

I have never liked to wear black. I think too many women seem to favor it, especially as they grow older.

Lighter colors, even white, are far more becoming to an older woman. In fact, light colors and carefully applied eye make-up can take years from almost any woman's age.

My taste in jewelry is just as definite. I like large, beautifully colored stones, and I am not concerned about their value. I also dote on handsome old settings.

I think that apart from Mademoiselle Chanel, the late Dame Edith Sitwell was the only person I ever knew who deliberately wore jewelry as a statement of her personality. I admired her for it. During one of her visits to America she lunched with me, and as we walked into the restaurant we must have made a most unusual sight. She was dressed in one of her favorite medieval robes and I wore an oriental creation, both of us sparkling with large, exotic gems —strands of unevenly graded pearls, heavy gold chains set with emeralds, huge baroque brooches. "I always carry my jewelry about in a steamer trunk," she said with a chuckle. "There was one time, on a lecture tour, just as I got off a train the trunk broke open on the platform and there I was, photographed in the middle of the debris! The caption read, 'Distinguished English poetess arrives with theatrical props.'"

A woman's choice of jewels reveals much about her personality. If I had been a tall, statuesque woman, I would probably have chosen tiny, delicate pieces. But since I am small and favor simple, even severely cut clothes, I feel they need the contrast of large colorful stones. My hair, too, is worn simply, but I bring to it the dramatic effect of necklaces and long earrings.

Although I no longer need the added courage that handsome jewelry once gave me (it was not easy being a hardworking woman in a man's world many years ago), I am aware that the wearing of exotic jewelry has become associated in many people's minds with the "image" of Helena Rubinstein, a mark of my identity, so to speak. And since I shall always love beautiful things, I feel I might as well enjoy wearing those I have.

For many years I was bothered with the problem of keeping this jewelry safe from would-be thieves yet in an accessible hiding place. At first I stored it in a Bergdorf Goodman dress box under my bed. Then my son Roy bought me a small safe. But I have always been clumsy with mechanical devices; besides, I could never remember the combination and would leave it around, written on pieces of paper. (I must add that I have never been very neat or tidy with my personal belongings. Moreover I am apt to be impatient when in a hurry.) Then one day, a wonderful friend and employee of mine, Sara Fox, devised the perfect solution. She bought me a large filing cabinet with many drawers. In the drawer marked D were stored all of my diamonds; under E could readily be found my emeralds; P was for pearls; R for rubies; S for sapphires and T for topaz. This is what I call a *klug* solution— a useful German word meaning clever.

8 Life Goes On

IT was spring of 1956. I had flown from New York to Paris and was waiting for Artchil who was to follow by sea, as he usually did. He never arrived. Roy broke the news to me that my husband had had a fatal heart attack.

I felt lost and inconsolable. I sat at Quai de Bethune looking out upon the most beautiful view in the world, mistress of much, but not of my own destiny. Artchil had loved life so! We had had so many plans, and there was so much we still wanted to do together. Later I learned that he had had several warnings from his doctor but had preferred to disregard them rather than worry me.

This was one time when I really did not know what to do. I was torn between wanting to fly back to America immediately—and never wanting to set foot there again! My doctor in Paris settled the problem for me. He gave me a strong sleeping draught and kept me quiet on sedatives to make sure that I would not get out of bed. A month must have passed during which time I was out of touch with my entire world, seeing only one or two members of my immediate family, my faithful secretary, my kindly staff.

Mercifully with time the desire for work returned. Letters had to be answered and decisions made. But all my interest in the House of Gourielli, which Artchil and I had started with such high hopes, vanished. I cabled instructions to Roy that the Gourielli building was to be sold. The thought of entering it again, with all of its memories, was more than I could bear.

I welcomed an urgent call to visit Rome, and from there, with my assistant for many years, Patrick O'Higgins, I went on to Israel. I wanted to see for myself this fascinating new country and to visit with my niece Rachel, Mala's sister. She had left Poland as a girl, to live in a kibbutz in the raw hills of what was then the divided land of Palestine, and for more than twenty years she had worked on a farm facing the Jordanian frontier, enduring untold hardship. Repeatedly I had urged her to join me in America, but her answer, although appreciative, was always the same: "I love this land and I cannot be separated from it."

Seeing Rachel again and her fine family of "Sabras," as the native-born Israeli are called (after a local cactus "hardy on the outside but sweetly soft within"), I was filled with a sense of hope for the future and an understanding which had forsaken me since Artchil's death. Even my own driving forces were lulled by a wonderful feeling of affection for a people whose only purpose in life was the development of a happy, self-sustaining community. For the first time in months I smiled, to see my Irish assistant, Patrick, as touched as I was myself by these hard-working, laughing, singing people who welcomed him and took him to their hearts.

Before leaving Israel I promised myself that one day I would build a memorial there, to commemorate this newfound peace. Today the Helena Rubinstein Art Pavilion in Tel Aviv is a small token of my admiration for what has been accomplished in Israel. It expresses also my feelings for Rachel, her family, and her fellow pioneers who gave so much to see their ideals of freedom become a reality.

Leaving Israel, we continued traveling around the world. I was still searching for forgetfulness, hoping that new countries, new faces would help to dull the old memories.

We flew everywhere. Our final objective, after having seen the great architectural wonders of India, Thailand, and Malaya, was Japan.

The Far East, especially Japan, had always fascinated and drawn me. Here was a land where women had achieved a degree of femininity almost unparalleled in any Western civilization. I am also a realist, however, and whenever I looked at the map of the world, noting where we had factories and thriving businesses, it had irked me to see that Japan remained a blank. I longed to build a plant there. It took only a few days in Tokyo to realize that the time was ripe. Strong competition had been established by several Japanese cosmetic firms whose yearly output was even greater than ours in America. This was all the challenge I needed. There was encouragement also from several charming Japanese ladies whom I met. They insisted that our methods and our products were far better suited to their skins than anything that was available in their country.

For three hectic weeks I held conferences and discussions with possible associates, attorneys, and bankers. The Japanese are an exceedingly courteous people, and it is not always easy to fathom their true feelings, certainly not for an Occidental. Nor are Japanese men accustomed to having business dealings with women. Fortunately I was an "elderly" woman, a Mama-San, and this commanded their respect. In due course our associates were decided upon, contracts signed, and an organization outlined on paper. Even so, it took nearly four years before our line of cosmetics could be launched in Japan; but that blank spot on the map had been filled, and I knew that with time my name and my business would become known in this most densely populated island on the face of the earth.

Hardly had I returned from my long trip around the world, undertaken primarily to help me forget the loss of the husband I had loved, than a second personal tragedy struck. Once more it came without warning. My younger son Horace, then in his middle forties, died suddenly in New York, of a heart attack. Horace had been the joy of my life. He had inherited his father's charm and good looks. His quick intelligence had delighted me although

101

I was conscious of his faults as well. We were much alike in character, impulsive, enthusiastic, sometimes overly credulous. I doted on my Horace. He had warmth and understanding. We worked together, sometimes disagreeing at first, but always in the end seeing eye to eye. From the time he was a small child he could wind me around his finger, and I knew of few greater pleasures.

The shock of Horace's death, following so closely on the loss of Artchil, crushed me to the point of inertia. This time the doctors and their sedatives were of no help. For weeks I would turn up at the office each morning, out of a lifelong habit. But I, who had always kept the door of my office open for any member of my staff to walk in at any time, now closed the door. The days were spent in simply sitting at my desk, doing nothing, brooding behind the closed door. If it had not been for my family and the many members of my staff who, I suspect, deliberately tried to keep my mind occupied with the day-to-day problems of the business, I know that I could not have continued.

It was a dear friend and associate, who had once been in love with Horace, who stirred me from my apathy. Sternly she said, "This must not go on, Helena. You are a matriarch. It is up to you to show us all how to behave."

Almost a decade has gone by since, easing the old wounds, producing new problems and new challenges and more often than not the painful awareness that with advancing years certain physical difficulties can only increase. If I have not dwelled much on illness in these pages it is because I am reluctant, as always, to think of the negative side of my life. I hate to give in, but there have been times, increasingly frequent in recent years, when it has been difficult for me to get out of bed, to dress and be on my way. The body is not a perfect instrument at best, and I have, after all, lived for nine decades. A major operation some years ago seemed to have marked a turning point in my life. The doctors were not very optimistic at the time, but I recovered. Was it will power? A love of life? Was I blessed with an unusually strong constitution, small though I am? What matters is that I am alive. The answer is in other hands—and in those hands I have often placed myself, with a brief prayer: "Dear God, keep me strong to do the things I must do."

Today I still manage to get to the office daily whether I am in London, Paris, New York, or any of our other centers. Once a week I drive out to our regional factory to work with our chemists in the laboratory. It is still my greatest passion to see a new product at its birth, to sample a new scent, to cover my hands or face with a possible new cream or lotion, to share in the work of my staff. It thrills me to watch products develop, to perfect and push them into the realm of actuality, so that from a formula they join the hundreds of certified Helena Rubinstein preparations bringing to women the world over a promise—and a fact.

I travel less, but I still enjoy having my family and friends about me for a game of bridge and a pleasant meal. True, I spend more time in bed and often wonder how I managed, years ago, to sleep so few hours without feeling a moment's fatigue. Yet my age in years bothers me very little. Even today my life is filled with what many people would consider "a full quota of activities." I wake up early, and my day begins. While still in bed, I have a breakfast tray, a newspaper, and the morning's mail which I read with interest—even the circulars!

By eight-thirty my secretary arrives, and together we examine the day's mail. Letters mean a great deal to me, not only as a means of communication but as a close link between two human beings. I read them with care and, unless they require further attention or discussion, I endeavor to answer them by return mail. While my secretary is with me, I often have a visit from my son Roy, my nephew Oscar Kolin, my principal American lawyer, Harold Weill. Here in my bedroom we can informally discuss important company policy. Since they all live nearby, it is a great convenience to hold these conferences at home, first thing in the morning, before we go off to our offices. Perhaps because of the informality of these meetings we sometimes accomplish more than we would have at an official office meeting involving divisional managers, sales managers, brand managers . . . our whole hierarchy.

Over the years I have always preferred to deal with a

small staff. Large meetings irritate me because of the waste of time involved in several people wanting to speak at once. I remember the pleasure of working with one chemist on a new formula, with one art director and one copywriter on an advertising campaign, with one accountant balancing our books or preparing a financial statement. But as our business has grown, more and more people have inevitably become a part of the necessary equipment. I take pride in this expansion. I am, after all, a "matriarch"—but I know from past experience that with a small staff we often managed to do our work more quickly.

In the morning from my bed (unless I have an early appointment which requires my getting up and dressed) I will also talk on the phone to friends and business associates, until I rise around ten, for my bath and personal beauty routine. I do not like the telephone and to this day cannot manage to dial a number correctly by myself. But I use it, since I must, to remind those around me that I am still interested in what they are doing and what they are thinking.

While still in the bath (I love a few drops of perfumed oil in the water) and with one of our good moisturizing creams on my face, I do simple stretching exercises to limber up. The steam from the warm water increases the moisturizing effect of the cream, softening my skin so that make-up foundation, rouge, and powder can be applied with an evenness that produces a truly natural look. While I make up, a maid brushes my hair and helps me to set it in my perennial chignon. There are times when I would have liked a more frilly hairdo, but I have always been a bit short on patience where my appearance was concerned, and besides, the day awaits me—decisions, people, and time slipping by.

Since the deaths of Artchil and Horace I have found it impossible to remain in one place for any great length of time. In 1959, for instance, I was delighted to accept the invitation of the American State Department to help represent the U.S. cosmetic industry at the American National Exhibition in Moscow. I knew that it would mean an arduous trip, but it would also mean an escape from myself. It was an important assignment. We were to demonstrate our methods of beauty culture and make-up to a vast audience of Russian women. I am far from being politically minded, but I have always believed that if anything could break the ideological barriers, beauty could. With the few words of Russian I had learned from Artchil years ago, and with the capable assistance and understanding of my niece Mala and a fine staff of Russian-speaking American beauticians to teach and demonstrate, I felt sure that we could help establish a feeling of friendship with the Russian women—which would, in turn, have its effect upon the more calculating male politicians.

We arrived in Moscow a few days before the official opening of the fair. My last visit to Russia had been in 1936 during the Stalin purges, and for a moment, as we set foot on Russian soil, I had a strange feeling of being stimulated and at the same time smothered.

Russia, to a Pole like myself, represents great power, at once magnificent and evil. I was conscious of this atmosphere when our little group flew into Moscow in the summer twilight, but I kept silent. Our reception was cordial, but it alarmed me to see our passports and plane tickets being whisked away as we were clearing customs. And worse was to come. We were a party of seven, Mala, my sister Ceska, and our various colleagues, but for some unknown reason we were all housed in different hotels. This made communication among us impossible, since Russian telephones operate on a mysterious digit system and our interpreters always seemed to vanish when they were most needed. But I refused to be intimidated. On that first night I went alone to the hotel restaurant where I ordered what promised to be a superlative meal. It was delicious when it finally arrived—two hours later! Caviar, Russian borscht, chicken à la Kiev, with the most fragrant, freshly baked bread and the creamiest ice cream imaginable. In time I was located by my little group, sitting beneath the ornate decorations of a huge, impersonal dining room, and we decided to celebrate our arrival, and our reunion, with Crimean champagne. By then I knew that whatever the problems, our stay in Moscow would be challenging but exciting.

The fair was officially opened several days later at Sokilniki Park, by Premier Khrushchev and Vice President Nixon. I recall walking a great distance, through umbrella-like pine trees, until we reached the Helena Rubinstein Pavilion. Everything was ready. Our Russian-speaking girls in their immaculate smocks stood ready with welcoming smiles, behind counters crowded with our products and with beauty literature especially printed in Russian. I joined them, whispering words of encouragement, and watched the proceedings. Later I was told that I should have been seated in one of the official stands, but it gave me a feeling of pride and security to be with my staff and to be close to the Russian women who crowded around, rather than a distant and official spectator.

Premier Khrushchev and Vice President Nixon gave us only a cursory glance as they toured the fair. They had bigger fish to fry. But as the hordes of women surrounded our small kiosk I remember thinking that politicians come and go . . . but there will always be women! It was not only their yearning for beauty advice and samples of our products which moved me practically to tears. A handsome middle-aged woman suddenly appeared at my side, and in a hurried whisper told me that she was a cousin of Artchil's. She went on to say how much it meant to her to meet me and what it meant to all Russian women to be introduced to modern American beauty methods. Then without another word she melted back into the crowd, and I could not find her again. Yet out of the entire trip to Russia, the work and the dedication that went into it, that one fleeting moment with my husband's unknown cousin meant more to me than all the subsequent praise I was to receive from official quarters.

On my return from Russia there was a recurrence of the old restlessness. I felt a strong desire to be in London and to have a home there. Many happy years of my early life had been spent in London with my first husband, with my two sons (like true Londoners, they had both been born "within the sound of Bow Bells") and with my sister Ceska, who is now in charge of our English business. Having a home in England would bring me closer to the past, I thought, while I could keep myself busy with such a mass of details that I would have little time to think of anything else, least of all myself.

Since setting up my London home, with every visit I am more aware that England has become a great creative center where new, young ideas are welcomed. Here I feel young again, and if I had the youthful proportions of today I would certainly buy most of my clothes in London. They are contemporary. It may be that I am a little tired of the endless Paris showings, the exhausting fittings, and the high prices. But it is not only clothes that I admire in England; it is something in the air, the enthusiasm of getting things done. In the arts the English painters, even the "pop" painters, make me want to start a new and current collection. The cinema, the books, magazines, even the newspapers give me a lift when I am in London. But what I most admired, a few years ago, was what was being done in the field of interior design and decoration for contemporary living. I wanted to live in London, and I wanted to see what could be done from scratch in furnishing a new home for myself there.

It took several weeks of searching before I found a suitable empty flat, thinking to myself at the time, how many women have gone through this same form of torture! Money is undoubtedly an asset in many ways, but public knowledge of one's wealth can be as great an obstacle as a limited budget is to the average housewife. I must have seen a hundred flats, from the most extravagant penthouses in Grosvenor Square to the "off-beat"—full of charm, some full of inconveniences, all full of rent. With Ceska's help and the experienced counsel of our London manager, Boris Forter, we finally came upon two floors in a fine Edwardian building in Knightsbridge. The rooms were poorly laid out, but I could see that with a few alterations the place had exciting possibilities.

Many a time I have seen a packaging idea in embyro, the skeleton of an advertising campaign, a dilapidated old house or a derelict piece of land on which I knew I could build. Somehow over the years my eyes have gained experience; and even though the consulting architects assured me that the Knightsbridge flat was hopeless, I liked it, and I sensed that something interesting could be done with it.

Unbelievable luck and a chance meeting with a brilliant young decorator gave me the assurance I needed. I had met David Hicks in the Albany flat of an old friend, Fleur Cowles. His frank enthusiasm and his clearly stated ideas on the subject of decoration intrigued me. We made an appointment to see the Knightsbridge premises together, and while there he sketched a rough plan, outlining his suggestions. That was when I signed the lease and gave Mr. Hicks the job of converting and decorating the entire flat.

Compared to my other homes in New York and Paris, the Knightsbridge apartment is small and compact. There are three bedrooms, and the living room doubles as a dining room. It is definitely a contemporary home, one that can easily be run with a minimum staff, since it contains every labor-saving device available. I was delighted with the purple living-room walls as a setting for some of my abstract paintings. I loved the room dividers of bronze and glass, on which some of my African sculptures, lit cleverly from above, glowed as if set with uncut stones. And yet, like so many other women, I was not happy with the kitchen. The shelves were narrow, there was little storage space; and the lighting was efficient but harsh. I hope that Mr. Hicks learned from me, as I did from him, about the necessity for decorators to study not only the client's taste but the housewife's needs.

One of my greatest joys in my new London home is the small canopied terrace planted with flowering shrubs. Its view commands the lovely green elegance of Hyde Park and a strangely romantic skyline with massed chimney pots, alarming new glass buildings, and the delicate spires of an occasional church seen in the distance. Here I love to sit as dusk falls . . . thinking, re-evaluating, plotting, in so far as I can, the uncertain course of my future. Death, if and when I think of it, frightens me no more and no less than it would anyone of my age. Besides, I have always been so concerned with living that it is difficult for me to imagine the hereafter. I cannot claim to having been religious in my life but, in my own way, I do believe that what has been done in this world will somehow be evaluated in the next. Rewarded? Punished? These are heavy words, and I am too old to play with them.

Although I have often said that I do not like looking back—why do I write this book? My purpose was not so much to tell the story of my life chronologically, for the record; but as a teacher I felt that a prelude was needed to the factual lessons in beauty which follow, and which I am anxious to share with every woman who is interested in making the most of herself.

Part Two

FOR BEAUTY

1 } Beauty Is Your Destination

SUCCESS can be measured by many standards. As I look back upon more than seventy years in the beauty business, I believe that my own success is due primarily to a combination of luck, hard work, and perseverance. But nothing really enduring in life, or in business, is ever done entirely alone. I have faith in the essentially American utilization of "team work"; I know that without the constant help of a large family, of thousands of devoted employees, of good friends in every walk of life, I could never have seen the fulfillment of the great adventure which started, humbly, as a one-room beauty salon in a provincial Australian city and grew into a world-wide industry.

With my family, with my colleagues (whom I look upon as a second family), from senior executives to "my little girls," as I am fond of calling the young, new generation of trainees in our business, I can share the ultimate satisfaction of knowing that we have truly contributed to the happiness of women all over the world. We helped to open their eyes to their potentialities by teaching them about beauty in a logical fashion, step by step, and creating products to enhance their beauty.

Of course, anyone who dedicates a lifetime to beauty care must have a strong desire, a true vocation, to create the finest, most effective products. It would be presumptuous of me to claim that my products are the only good ones. There are many reputable cosmetic companies with excellent products. For this reason I tell women seeking my advice, "Select what best suits you! But once you have done so, stick to it!"

In the pages that follow I shall tell you about certain beauty products that I believe in, and try to describe the best methods of applying them to achieve what I feel are the most beneficial, long-lasting results.

My greatest concern is to help you establish a regular pattern of beauty care. The first step can only be achieved by following healthful living habits. Good health comes first. Beauty is a matter of developing the right attitude—and of doing something about it.

For many years I have asked myself: "Why is it so easy to persuade a pretty woman to do something more for herself, but so hard to start a plain woman doing anything?"

Why does Elizabeth Taylor, for instance, admit to taking an hour and a half to dress (and I have seen her, in a studio peignoir, without make-up, her hair disheveled, yet looking so beautiful that even the movie crews milling about her were starry-eyed), while a less brilliantly endowed woman, who should lavish time on herself, takes a mere ten minutes?

The answer comes from within the individual. It is a question, quite simply, of negative, lazy thinking.

Doers are rare! Many women dream vaguely of being beautiful, of having a "look" that will make people turn their heads and think, "I wonder who she is? What an exciting-looking woman!"

Yes, they would adore this, provided they could achieve it with no effort. But life isn't that easy, not even in matters of beauty. Here, too, one must give to get. One must become aware that the achievement of beauty takes time, thought, and effort—surely not too much when you consider the stakes. Isn't it worth a little effort on your part to win them?

This second part of my book is my "beauty testament."

It is a collection of the best ideas and methods in beauty care as practiced in my salons everywhere. Some are new, others have remained unchanged throughout the years because their effectiveness has been proved beyond question. I believe in them. I have seen the remarkable results that have been brought about by their regular, consistent use.

There are no secrets in beauty care. We must work together to rediscover these ideas and apply them to you. They can be your windows on a new world, a world filled with possibilities and the very best that the science of beauty care has to offer you.

I need not see you or look into your eyes to read the little plaguing doubts that are already passing through your mind. How many times I have heard a woman say, "Is there really something you can do about my skin? Nothing seems to work." Or, "Madame Rubinstein, you have no idea how troubled I am about my hair. It's impossible to manage!"

Then there are the silent ones who don't even voice their anxieties and fears. They come into the salon hesitantly, they look, they remain uncertain—all the time their eyes plead to be persuaded to make the right move toward beauty. They seem to be related in some way to the women with sun-parched skins whom I first met in Australia at the turn of the century. They had left the lovely dewiness of their skins in Europe, but in my first cream they suddenly saw a flicker of hope.

When a woman thinks she is plain, someone or something has caused this feeling. We must root it out like a weed and put a new, tender plant called hope in its place; maybe even something stronger than hope—trust, confidence, and belief.

In all my years of helping women to find their heritage of beauty, I can only say that I have never met a woman who really cared about being alluring and lovely, and who tried to achieve these twin objectives, who failed to do so.

Here are a few of the root causes of plainness (Horace would have called them "shackles of the spirit") which prevent otherwise intelligent women from reaching their objective of beauty.

   ✓ They believe that beauty is the equivalent of sin.

✔ They've been made to feel beauties are made in heaven and not actually on earth as, of course, they are.

✔ They had selfish mothers who kept them feeling plain so *they* could monopolize the admiration.

✔ They were taunted or teased by brothers or sisters at a sensitive age, and so retreated from thinking about their own appearance.

Often, at a social gathering, I am approached by one of the male guests who says laughingly, "Tell me, is it really true that you can make a woman over? Transform her?" Then, as I nod assent, comes the usual quip: "Perhaps I should send my wife to you."

I never bother to explain to these doubting Thomases that we don't really do over a woman like papering a room or reupholstering furniture. In reality we try to help the woman find herself. We organize a program of activities that will gradually change her externally and set up habits that will help her find her new look and discover a new way of doing things. If we are lucky (and she is too), the belief will grow in her that beauty *is* attainable

In the New York salon we feature "A Day of Beauty" to give a woman a taste of the rich rewards of concentrated care, a chance to actually see for herself what eight hours of special attention to skin, make-up, circulation, and diet can do. The end results are always a joyful surprise to a woman who has never realized her own potential, who has neglected to care for herself. Suddenly, having glimpsed her new glamorous self, she yearns for more. Now she has the proof before her that she is a creature of endless possibilities.

I recall the head of our Chicago salon telling me the story of a young woman journalist who used to drop into the salon to gather beauty material for her newspaper articles. Curiously, though she was reporting on beauty, she wore no make-up, did her own hair, and showed a general indifference to fashion. Finally the salon manageress broached the subject. "Tell me, Miss Whittier, why don't you do more for yourself? Don't you approve of make-up?" The salon manageress was stunned when the journalist replied, "There's nothing anyone can do about me. I'm just a plain Jane. I merely write about beauty."

My manageress told me she was at a loss for words but she tried to keep her surprise in check, answering, "Could you spare the time to spend a day in the salon? I'd like to show you something—*yourself*."

"Certainly," the young visitor replied, "but believe me, you're wasting your time."

That very day she had her first salon treatment. Her face, untouched by care, but with an amazingly fine-textured skin, was given first a complete facial with a mask treatment to bring out the clarity of tone and texture. A make-up artfully conceived by a master was applied over a sheer foundation. (It was hard to believe that this twenty-five-year-old girl had never used even a make-up foundation.) Her hair, a glossy brown with golden highlights, was softly waved in a classic casual style and shaped by deft professional hands. Her body was massaged, and as her circulation improved so did her skin tones. And so did the light in her eyes.

At the end of "A Day of Beauty" the same girl emerged. But was it she? "Even I," said my manageress, "could scarcely believe it. We had hatched," she told me, "a swan from an ugly duckling." The happy conclusion came about when she rushed in out of breath, two days later, to report to the manageress. "Miss Sartaine, do you know what happened to me? After you'd fixed me all up I had a date with my favorite man. He had been pretty indifferent lately. He took one look at me and said, 'What in the world happened to you? No, don't tell me, just keep on doing it. The new scenery is terrific!' "

This is more or less a standard beauty success story. Whenever a woman first realizes her hair is drab, her skin lacks clarity, that she is a little on the dumpy side—and wants to do something about it—she is on her way to the higher goal of beauty.

Now I know exactly what you are thinking. You've already worked up the perfect excuse! "Of course they can do all that in a salon with all those experts—but how can I do it here, now?"

The wonderful thing about experience is that it helps one to recognize the essentials. Because of a lifetime spent in solving beauty problems, I feel I can pin-point the elements that will set you on the right path, so that you can follow your search for beauty, whatever your circumstances.

I suggest as a first step a little self-analysis. Let's start with the leading question:

What do you think of your own looks? Before you answer, I'd like to recount an incident about a diplomat's daughter whom I knew quite well some thirty years ago in Paris. She entertained extensively in her lovely home. Her friends spoke of her admiringly as being a real beauty. She was considered incredibly glamorous. Yet one day she came to me and said, "Madame Rubinstein, I'm worried to death. You see, I have such a terribly greasy skin. My hair is hard to handle. My figure is hippy. My ankles are thick. Do you think there is anything at all that you could do for me? I'm afraid of losing my husband."

This was so farfetched that I might have laughed, had I not been aware that few people really know what they look like. Even actresses who receive tremendous adulation and applause seldom believe that it has anything to do with their looks. Hence objectivity, honesty, and candor are most necessary. There is always a grain of truth in what other people have said about you and to you. Here, again, self-analysis will solve many of your problems.

Are you perhaps average in looks? A little better than average? Accustomed to enthusiastic response? Or do you really feel that feature for feature, and all other things considered, you could hardly be called a beauty at this very moment?

Here is a check list to help you along with your own judgments:

HAIR	*Thick Luxuriant Glossy Lively Manageable Thin Dull Flyaway Uninteresting*
HEAD	*Well-proportioned Too small Too large Too long Too round Bumpy*
EYES	*Large Expressive Beautifully colored Long lashes Good brows Small Close together Dull Thin-lashed Scraggly brows*

NOSE	Straight Small Regular Fine nostrils Fine arch Tip-tilted Bumpy Large Irregular Large nostrils Too aquiline Snub nose
MOUTH	Expressive Flattering shape Suitable size Lips tight Upper lip narrow Lower lip narrow Upper lip too full Lower lip too full Mouth too big Too small Crooked
SKIN	Dry Oily Normal Combination Temperamental Acne Blemished Aging Clear Transparent Soft Smooth
CHIN	Just right Dimpled Free from double chins Balanced Too prominent Receding Nonexistent Fuzzy
NECK	Graceful Smooth Slender Long Corded Bony Short Fat
SHOULDERS	Straight Muscular Sloping Flabby Hunched
UPPER ARM	Graceful Firm Muscular Flabby
LOWER ARM	Slender Wrist well-proportioned Heavy Muscular Raw-boned Wrist large
HANDS	Smooth Expressive Graceful Long-fingered Slender Rough Awkward Short-fingered Fat
BUST	Uplifted Nicely shaped Firm Sagging Too large Too small Flabby
WAIST	Firm Slim Small Rigid Large Fat
HIPS	Slender Rounded Firm Flat Narrow Heavy Angular Flabby Thick Wide

KNEES	*Smooth Firm Slender Rough Flabby Heavy Stiff*
CALF	*Heavy Muscle-bound Bumpy Fuzzy Discolored Slender Long-muscled Clear-skinned*
ANKLE	*Small-boned Slender Flexible Big-boned Heavy Rigid*
FOOT	*Slender Flexible High arch Unblemished Squat Rigid Fallen arch Corns, calluses, bunions, etc.*

This check list is vitally important. Run through it carefully. Then it will become easy for you to see that, like every other woman, you have definite beauty assets and defects. You are no exception to the rule. Moreover, a clear path begins to open up.

Knowing oneself is not always easy. I have sometimes worn a dress which did not suit me; I have used a new make-up which was too high-keyed for my skin texture; I have even tried hair ornaments with disastrous results. We all make mistakes. Seldom do we wish to admit them! To prevent such mistakes I would like to suggest an amusing, informative hobby. It will take many weeks to perfect, but it is well worth the effort in enjoyment and, finally, in results.

Keep a scrapbook in which you paste photographs, articles, advertisements from magazines and newspapers which, for one reason or another, appeal to you. What a revelation such a scrapbook can be! It is not an original idea. In the eighteenth and nineteenth centuries most sensitive women kept such "memory" books, but the habit—and the art of doing so—went out of fashion with these modern days. Leisure is rare. There are so many other forms of entertainment!

A few years ago I realized how useful such a scrapbook could be. On a flight across the Atlantic I sat next to a woman who was one of the most photographed, admired, and talked-about leaders of fashion on both sides of the Atlantic.

Myself, when I first arrived in Australia at the turn of the century.

My mother *(seated, right)* and four of my sisters—Erna *(seated, left)* and *(standing)* Manka, Regina and Ceska.

Before leaving for
Australia in my teens.

Three years after open-
ing my Melbourne salon.

Riding in the Australian outback.

Photographed in Paris in the late 20s, my sister Manka, myself and my sister Stella.

Greenwich, Connecticut, with my sons Roy and Horace.

With my namesake, Roy's daughter Helena Titus, 1958.

Edward Titus

Artchil Gourielli

Working in my Paris laboratory.

My work day often started with morning coffee and dictating the mail from my bed.

The stairway of the London salon. The house was famous in Edwardian days when Mrs. Willie James, a close friend of King Edward VII, entertained there.

With my son Roy Titus when he was elected an officer of the American company.

With my niece Mala in front of St. Basil's church, Moscow.

Catholic charities have always interested me, and I have especially enjoyed working with the Maryknoll order.

Receiving the Cancer Committee's Sword of Hope Award from Mrs. Lester B. Robbins, Women's Activities co-chairman.

A visit to Holland's tulip fields inspired me to launch a tulip cosmetic line.

The Helena Rubinstein Pavilion of Contemporary Art in Tel Aviv.

·It was an honor to help Mrs. Roosevelt in her untiring work for cancer research.

Prime Minister David Ben-Gurion received me in Tel Aviv during my first visit to Israel.

With Elizabeth Taylor on the set of *Cleopatra* in Rome.

With Richard Burton on my terrace in New York.

Pablo Picasso started sketching me in 1958 for a portrait that never materialized.

I have been fortunate to be painted my many of the world's most talented artists.

Marcoussis, a Polish compatriot, did this engraving of me
in the early 1920s.

1934. Portrait by Marie Laurencin.

1942. Portrait by Salvador Dali.

1959. Portrait by Graham Sutherland.

1960. Portrait by René Bouché.

New York. The hallway at 625 Park Avenue.

New York. A corner of the living room.

New York. The Dali room.

New York. The small dining room.

New York. The living room, with Picasso's tapestry *Seated Women*.

New York. My bedroom.

Paris. The African collection.

Paris. A corner of my bedroom.

Paris. The "petit salon," with Renoir's *Bathers*.

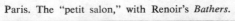

My bedroom at the Moulin.

The Moulin, my country home outside Paris.

I have always loved fashion, and having my clothes designed by famous couturiers has been one of my happiest
extravagances.

Left, my first ball gown by Worth. *Above*, a romantic tea
gown by Doucet.

On my return from a trip to Morocco in the early 30s I posed in a caftan and turban. The Valentino influence perhaps?

Left, Poiret was a genius. This dress, influenced by the Russian ballet, was one of his creations.

Schiaparelli created this blouse when she first opened her
maison de couture in Paris.

One of the first dresses made for me by Captain Molyneux.

The simplicity of Balenciaga's clothes was a good foil for the jewelry I have always loved to collect.

1964. Yves Saint-Laurent designed this lovely dress, which I wore for the first time this past Christmas Eve.

During our long flight she kept happily occupied pasting photographs and clippings, cut from various magazines, in a large scrapbook. I asked her why she was doing this. "It is my secret," she answered. "I have pasted my way into acquiring a fashion sense. Because of this fashion sense I have developed my own personality!"

"Years ago," she added, "I was suddenly very dissatisfied with the way I looked. None of the clothes I chose seemed to be right for me. I hated my hair style. Even my homes seemed dull, unimaginative, lacking in individuality. Then one weekend I saw a friend of mine compiling a scrapbook and the idea came to me that I should do the same thing. Only there was to be a difference. My scrapbook, instead of being filled with photographs of friends, holidays, of moments of happiness to be remembered, would deal only with ideas . . . feminine ideas such as the photographs of clothes I admired in magazines, the mouth-watering menus I came across in the newspapers, the original beauty secrets I found in French novels.

"But to do this I limited myself. I was very disciplined. Whatever I saw or read had to appeal to me fully at *that* very moment. Six months from the day that I first started my scrapbook I decided to analyze what was in it. And do you know, my likes, and therefore my dislikes, were clearly mirrored to me on every page. For instance, I was consistent in my love for the classical. There were dozens of photographs of Greek marbles, of draped dresses, classical hair styles, and Mycenaean golden ornaments.

"Because of my scrapbook I realized that there was a frightening difference between the clippings pasted in it and what, until then, I had chosen to surround myself with, dress myself in. I eliminated nine-tenths of my possessions. I even economized by doing so. But what is best of all, I developed a very clear vision of my taste and was able to formulate the direction I wished to take to express it."

Why don't you try this system which my flight companion found to be so successful? Her name was Mrs. Reginald Fellows. Each generation produces only *one* Mrs. Fellows, but the heritage of such a great individualist should be enjoyed by all, even in lesser degrees.

I like this anecdote and often quote it because it is constructive. A scrapbook will show you what direction your subconscious is taking. It will help you to develop style—your own instinctive style, which is the essence of fashion and one of the secrets of beauty. But you must be consistent. You must be determined to keep it up to date. You must be, as I am fond of telling so many people, *strong*.

For years, in every one of my advertisements, I insisted on a line of copy which is still very dear to my heart, "There are no ugly women, only lazy ones." Remember this.

But now, let us begin with *beautiful skin*.

2 Beauty Begins with Your Skin

How fortunate you are to be living in today's world! It seems to me only yesterday that I was a girl, and beauty care was a private and personal matter, not to be discussed outside the bedroom. As a result, beauty was in the hands of a few amateurs or housewives with a gift for concocting their own lotions and potions. And they had to be bribed to secrecy, for no one must know that feminine beauty was aided by anything but Nature!

In my lifetime I have seen great changes in the formulation of skin care preparations—many of them of my own making. Not the least of these was based on observation of my very first clients in Melbourne, many years ago, when I realized how much one type of skin differs from another.

I have constantly sought out and worked with doctors and scientists in laboratories throughout the world, so that every woman could have a smooth, lovely complexion whatever her skin type or her special problem.

When you know your own skin and recognize its needs, you can begin to give it the proper care. The next move, then, is to decide which of the following skin types is yours.

Dry Skin. This is by far the most prevalent type of skin. Somehow it seems to fit too tightly over the bones —it is drawn, it flakes, cracks, and is susceptible to chapping. A network of fine lines shows up which, if neglected, soon turns into furrows and deep lines. There are so many factors which affect this type of skin: dry heat indoors, exposure to sun, driving in the wind, and time itself! With advancing years the natural oil and moisture in the skin lessen, pinching in lines and exaggerating wrinkles. But this problem is not unique with the past-thirties. Many women find they have to wage a constant war against dry skin from the teens upward.

Oily Skin. Here the oil glands are working overtime. The oily or sebaceous glands produce more oil than is needed and it oozes up constantly, giving the face a greasy shine and coarsening the pores. Even worse, it catches and holds dust and grime which clogs oil ducts— and here you have the origin of unsightly blackheads.

Acne-blemished Skin. Nobody has to tell the girl with acne-blemished skin what her problem is. She knows. And the worst of it is that neglect is serious since the skin may become permanently pitted and scarred.

Sensitive Skin. Reacts almost nervously to both external and internal changes. Sometimes it behaves itself surprisingly well; then, almost without warning, it shows a flushed or reddened look. Unaccountably it may itch. And when it flushes it does so quickly and unevenly. It is a maddening skin, with no sense of timing. It will choose the very moment you want to look your best to behave at its worst.

Combination Skin. This is one of the most frequently misunderstood and mistreated skins. Do you recognize it as being your special bête noire? Dry and taut, with even a little powdery flakiness, along cheekbones and forehead, yet often it seems to pour oiliness at the nostrils, the tip of the nose, the area between the lower lip and the chin. Result—a dry outer frame to the face and a center panel with unappealing clusters of blackheads and enlarged pores along the nose and above the chin.

Normal Skin. Occasionally in the younger woman I encounter a normal skin. It has a soft velvety texture, no oily pockets to mar its tender transparency. Color glows under its translucent surface almost as the light that diffuses through my treasured opaline glass. Fingers glide across it silkily. In every light, at every turn, it is a fleeting joy. Because it is as beautiful as it is, it must be tended and cared for if it is to last.

Aging Skin. This is a "time tired" skin. Oh yes, time does diabolical things to the skin—or haven't you noticed? Some days you sigh and say, "My face is positively pasty; I don't like the way I look any more." Then you begin to notice those little monitors of passing days, the clusters of tiny wrinkles and crisscross lines, and the skin about your throat that appears to sag.

But courage. There is much to be gained if you have the interest in giving your particular skin the care it needs.

Dry skin must be moisturized and lubricated.

Oily skin needs scrupulous cleansing and refining.

Acne-blemished skin requires meticulous cleanliness and medication.

Sensitive skin, like sensitive people, must be treated with kindliness, gently soothed with bland beauty aids.

Combination skin must be coaxed toward balance by double treatment—the techniques for coping with oily skin and dry skin used simultaneously in the needed areas.

Normal skin should be treasured and preserved with regular, sensible care.

Aging skin needs moisture and rich night creams. It must also be assisted with such "look younger" aids as stimulating lotions and creams.

Now for most of you—unless you live in remote communities—an easy and satisfactory way to get an analysis of your skin condition is to visit one of my salons. They are to be found in most of the capitals of the world, with a staff of trained specialists who will be glad to explain in detail—*at no charge*—the correct treatment required for your particular skin. They will outline the most essential preparations so you can begin to care for your skin yourself in a day-to-day program of self-improvement. They are there to help you, and you can rest assured no one will be offended if you don't wish to buy the preparations recommended by the expert analyst.

Another good place to obtain help in identifying your skin problems and selecting the special preparations designed to help them is the cosmetic department of a large department store. Very often a demonstrator is there who has been personally trained by my staff, and who can show you how to care for your skin down to the very last little upward stroke of your fingers.

And in this day and age, when the distribution of cosmetics is as widespread as medicine, drugstores very often have an advisory cosmetician who is familiar with the most important preparations and will be happy to guide you in the selection of the ones you need most.

Even though the scientific aids to beauty and the facts are available to most women, I find from the mail that floods my office daily that the women in more remote places need and want information. For them there is no one close at hand to answer their questions.

For example, a lady in a hill town in Pakistan writes: "Dear Madame Rubinstein, My daughter is just fourteen and her skin is rough and unsightly. I believe she may be suffering from acne but I don't really know. Most of my life it has been sufficient for me to use milk and lentil flour, and my skin has always been smooth and soft as silk. But now my child is so embarrassed. What can I do for her?"

A girl from Iran printed the following message: "There is so much I do not know. My skin flakes and hurts when the sand blows against it. Can I make it stronger?"

A young girl from a small town in central France confides: "Everyone talks about cars and planes and how easy it is to get about. But I still walk to town and the local druggist doesn't seem to know how to stop my skin from looking so rough. Besides, I have dark fuzz on my cheeks and upper lip, and the young men here do not admire me."

It is because of the millions of women like these that I include certain factual data that may be obvious to some of you. It is my conviction that wise care of the skin comes from a real understanding of the skin itself. Besides, I must admit that the cause of skin problems has always held my deepest interest.

Did you know, for instance, that the skin acts chiefly as a protective covering for the body and that it performs this protective function through a complex series of biological processes? The skin is actually an organ which secretes and excretes and which simultaneously regenerates itself in an orderly fashion. It is extremely sensitive to both external and internal changes. Although its structure is complex, it consists basically of two distinct layers—the outer layer or epidermis, and the under layer or dermis. The texture, color and health of the outer skin are simply an outward sign of what goes on in the underlying dermis.

When you realize clearly that the skin you would like to change on the outside is being affected by the layers inside, then you know why beauty care has become a real science. Nobody, least of all myself, is content any longer with being "surfacy." We constantly delve deeper to learn the secrets of the inner skin.

We have discovered conclusively that the skin is a moisture lover, internally and externally. Parch it, burn it, dry it out, and it shows its rage by deteriorating rapidly. It is astounding how quickly a skin responds if you drink three pints of water a day. This water cure helps to clear impurities from the system feeding the skin.

Preparations are formulated these days to renew as well as possible the skin's protective oils, to conserve its natural moisture, and to stimulate it. The pores, those tiny open mouths on the skin's surface, drink up these moisturizing elements and throw a light, protective film over the skin. In this way an oil-moisture balance is maintained which is one of the basic sources of a naturally beautiful complexion.

I was delighted to find in a recent survey by a large department store in the United States that the single beauty preparation most in demand was the moisturizer. Ten years ago this could have happened only in my imagination. Now most women have awakened to the greatest single need of their skins—moisture!

Though the treatment of each skin type differs, the technique I have developed remains the same. Once you've learned to use your hands and fingers to help relax, soothe, and massage the contours of your face, it's like learning to swim—you never forget it.

Here are my salon methods of applying creams and lotions. Why not practice them until they have become second nature to you?

Helena Rubinstein Salon Methods of Applying Skin-Care Preparations

To Apply Liquid Cleanser

Rotate on the skin until cleanser turns creamy white. Remove with tissues.

To Apply All Creams

Use both hands and stroke with an upward motion (a) from chin to ears, (b) from nose to temples, (c) up between the eyes and out over the eyelids. Follow the same movements when removing cream with tissues.

For the throat: Always use smooth upward motions in applying throat cream or oil. Then massage with rotary motions, increasing pressure on the upstrokes. Use right hand to stroke left side of neck and left hand for right side.

For Flabby Chin: Use backs of both hands and pat firmly under chin, working from center out toward ears.

For the Eyes: An eye cream should be (a) smoothed on over the eyelids and (b) with very light strokes "fingerprinted" under the eyes from outer corner to inner corner. (To "fingerprint" pat lightly, using two fingers alternately.)

To Apply Lotion

Saturate a pad of cotton with lotion. Apply all over face; then pat well on skin with an upward lift.

To Apply a Stimulant

Saturate a pad of cotton and press firmly on relaxed muscles under chin, from ear to ear, then (a) quickly back and forth across entire throat. (b) Press lightly on face with upward motion; puff out cheeks and press on expression lines. (c) Press on frown lines between eyes and across-forehead lines. Apply gently under eyes.

160

Wet face thoroughly with warm water; pour wash in wet palm of hand. Apply with both hands and work into the skin with upward, outward motions. If a lather is desired, add more water as needed. Rinse off thoroughly and pat dry with towel.

Custom Beauty Care for Your Skin

Are you ready to assign five minutes a day, or possibly a little more, to making the most of your skin? Regular daily care must become a habit, as automatic as brushing your teeth. It's not enough to fix your face once in a while, in a flurry of excitement. If you want to look beautiful, you will have to tend your skin every day.

And it's worth it! Your skin will smile every time you smile. It will make people doubt your birth date. Even if you haven't a single perfect feature, with a lovely translucent skin you will always be remembered as a pretty woman.

Each step in your skin-care program is planned scientifically, and for best results you should follow through to the letter.

Dry skin is far and away the most common of all types. It exists in young and old, in men as well as in women. But it's easy to cope with, because the problem is simply one of lubricating and moisturizing. Properly done, this "treatment" should take no more than five minutes a day.

My Beauty Regime for Dry Skin
(See page 160 for complete method of application)
Morning

1. Cleanse with a concentrated cleanser that reaches deeply into the skin and removes every trace of grime and make-up (even eye make-up). It's unbelievable what you will find was on your face when you tissue off.

2. Now you refresh with a mild astringent lotion that's cooling and fragrant too. Moisten a cotton pad with the lotion and go over the path of the cleanser to remove the last trace of cream.

3. Finish with an emulsion moisturizer. You dot this on, then spread it over the face with your fingers, dabbing on a little extra wherever the skin is driest. All day long this additional moisture invisibly protects your skin under your make-up.

Night

Repeat the same cleansing and freshening—but as a final step treat your dry skin to a rich, emollient moisturizing cream that works deeply to end skin dryness. It disappears into the skin because modern science has found a way to give more lubrication without greasiness! Now you can look pretty at bedtime and even prettier on awakening in the morning.

MY BEAUTY REGIME FOR OILY SKIN
(See page 160 for complete method of application)

An oily, shiny skin makes many a young woman miserable. This condition, unless corrected, can last a lifetime, but loving care under expert direction and started early can assure a fresh, translucent skin. I know this, because I was one of the first to treat oily skin problems and the accompanying problems of clogged pores and blackheads. I created a special wash containing small granules to loosen pore-clogging impurities which often turn into blackheads.

Morning and Night

1. Wash oily skin thoroughly with a medicated cream wash. On it goes—off it goes, and with it goes the oiliness you don't want. It also contains an antiseptic which inhibits the growth of blemish-causing bacteria. Your skin is left soft, immaculate, without a hint of oil.

2. Tone the skin with a medicated astringent skin lotion to leave your skin looking smoother and finer. You pat the lotion on wherever oil and shine are most apt to appear. (It is a good idea to keep this lotion with you during the day, to be used as a spot refresher and cleanser. Its astringent qualities are mild, so it can be used frequently.) Your make-up will go on more smoothly, with a soft matte finish.

Two or three times a week

Wash with the soluble, friction-creating granules that reach deeply into pore openings to rout out blackheads and free clogging impurities so they can be flushed out. Moisten the grains in the palm of your hand. Work into a lather on your wet face. Rinse off.

MY BEAUTY REGIME FOR ACNE-BLEMISHED SKIN

The cause of acne has not been definitely established, but it is usually accompanied by excessive oiliness which can be intensified by a diet rich in chocolate, cocoa, salt, nuts, candy, fats, gravies, sauces and spices. Other detrimental factors seem to be infected teeth, tonsils or sinuses, and often emotional stress.

It is a scientific fact that healthy skin renews itself regularly, by throwing off dead skin cells to reveal the healthy new skin underneath. One of the times it happens is when you wash. You wash away dead skin and also the oil produced by the oil glands in your skin.

In skin troubled by acne, the oil glands produce too much oil too quickly. The excess oil and dead skin cells form a crust, plugging up oil inside the pores. These plugs are blackheads, scientifically called comedones. When irritated and infected, they become pimples.

This type of skin needs to have its oil output reduced and natural peeling encouraged. Above all, it must be kept clean.

Morning

1. Wash your hands thoroughly before you begin. Splash warm running water over your face several times. Now, since you want to rid the skin of surface oil that has been clogging your pores, wash your face carefully with a special medicated lathering cleanser which inhibits the growth of blemish-causing bacteria and helps to prevent a new outbreak. Rinse off. The splash-away technique is best. Don't use washcloths; they could give shelter to the very bacteria you want to evict.

2. Now press on a cooling, mildly astringent medicated lotion that reduces the oiliness which can cause break-outs.

3. Apply a clearing medicated cream by dotting each pimple with it. It is skin-tinted and greaseless, so it won't show. It speeds up gentle, natural peeling of acne pimples. It reduces the accumulation of excess oil which is a prime trouble maker in acne conditions. Its antiseptic action inhibits the growth of blemish-causing bacteria, helps pre-

163

vent the spread of infection and the formation of new acne pimples.

Night

Repeat the same process!

NOTE: You should also use a medicated shampoo suitable for oily and acne-blemished skins, one which removes excessive oils and controls dandruff-causing bacteria which may aggravate acne pimples.

As a rule I prefer to think of the "do's" about the skin —not about the don'ts. It's more constructive and forward thinking. But there is one very important "don't." *Don't, please don't squeeze!* Even if you manage to open a pimple it could spread infectious material. And what's more dangerous, you could cause permanent scarring. It's better to treat pimples consistently with medicated cream, to dry them up.

One of the greatest satisfactions of my career has been to introduce my medicated preparations to young people who have suffered from the problems of acne. Acne often vanishes altogether as time itself reduces the oily output of the skin—in the meantime, however, these young people can be saved hours of anguish. They can enjoy the pleasures of having a skin others like to look at and touch.

MY BEAUTY REGIME FOR A SENSITIVE SKIN

(See page 160 for complete method of application)

Your skin is temperamental? First pale, then flushed? Does it sometimes break out in patches? Is it unaccountably oily and then dry? It may be reflecting your own inner ups and downs. Try to get extra rest. Drink a great deal of water. Learn to relax. Try listening to music, or reading in bed, with your feet raised on two pillows. Most important of all, take the most scrupulous care of this skin that shows its reactions so obviously. Handle it gently. Never rub or pull.

Morning

1. Cleanse with a fluid deep cleanser that glides on lightly and cleans deeply without your having to rub and tug at your tender skin. Apply gently with upward rotating movements. Tissue off.

2. Soothe with a gentle herbal and honey extrait lotion,

one that will cool and comfort sensitive smarting skin, and overcome flakiness too. (During the day bathe your face with this "extrait" whenever it feels hot and tense.)

3. Now moisturize with a light dewy emulsion. Your make-up will go on more smoothly than ever before.

Night

1. Cleanse with deep cleanser as in the morning.
2. Soothe with the same herbal lotion.
3. Lubricate with a light moisturizing cream, preferably one that contains skin collagen protein, a natural ingredient comparable to the proteins of young skin.

MY BEAUTY REGIME FOR COMBINATION SKIN
(See page 160 for complete method of application)

Combination skins are very common. The skin on the cheeks is rather dry, while the center panel, forehead, nose and chin, have a tendency toward oiliness.

Morning

1. Cleanse with the deep cleanser that floats away impurities.
2. Reduce oiliness, brace and tone the center panel (forehead to nose to chin) by pressing on a freshening, refining lotion.
3. Moisturize the dry areas with a moisturizing emulsion that makes the driest skin feel dewy to the touch. Make-up will go on beautifully and stay fresher too.

Night

1. Repeat Step 1.
2. *Twice weekly* gently wash the oily center panel of the face with organic washing grains to keep the pores from clogging, release oils, and free blackheads.

On alternate nights freshen by pressing on the same astringent oil-reducing lotion used in the morning.

3. Smooth dry areas with a richly emollient moisturizing cream.

MY BEAUTY REGIME FOR NORMAL SKIN
(See page 160 for complete method of application)

If you are fortunate enough to have this precious gift, a naturally beautiful skin, lavish it with loving care. You are one of the lucky ones. You have a head start in your efforts to protect your beauty. It's always easier to take care of a healthy normal skin than to correct a skin problem.

But do bear this in mind—a normal, well-behaved skin can move in one of two directions: 1) toward keeping translucent and lovely or, 2) toward drying up and developing lines and wrinkles. And if not cleansed scrupulously, it can become coarse. The choice is yours.

Morning and Night

✓ Cleanse with a light penetrating cleanser.

✓ Pat on a freshening skin-toning lotion.

✓ Keep your skin dewy with a moisturizing emulsion under your make-up.

As you grow a little older simply add a rich emollient moisturizing cream to your treatment. But right now the word for you is *moisturize*. When you are in a rush, just cleanse and then use a moisturizer. Never, never be caught without a moisturizer!

I'm sure you will understand that as a world-famous authority on beauty and skin care I am especially anxious to postpone the look of age. Not only because as a woman I enjoy being admired, but as a professional I wouldn't think of presenting a tired, faded face to the world. Generally speaking, I've always been taken for at least twenty years younger than I am. Now, at ninety-plus, I do not expect to look like a young woman, but I still find it amusing and flattering to be thought younger than I am.

In later years the skin loses its elasticity and flexibility. As the skin ages, the outer layer becomes drier, due to lessened oil secretion and decreased moisture. The skin tends to be thinner and lines and wrinkles develop. In a woman, these physiological changes in the skin are closely associated with the altered or reduced production of the female hormones, estrogen and progesterone. A few minutes spent each night and morning treating your skin can delay the encounter with age indefinitely. With massage and stimulants you can help your contours to resist time and your skin to stay smooth and youthful-looking longer. The further past forty you go, the more minutes you spend on yourself, the lovelier results your face will show.

(See page 160 for complete method of application)
Morning

1. Smooth a few drops of cleansing cream or lotion over face and neck, always moving in upward strokes. Start at the base of the neck and go straight up to the chin and over the face.

2. Tissue off cleanser and freshen with a soothing, non-drying skin lotion enriched with herbals.

3. Apply a rich moisturizing emulsion. On days when your skin seems to drink it in with extra speed, use this dewy liquid a second time. It's invisible on the skin.

Night

1. Cleanse as described above.

2. Now pat upward with a cotton pad saturated with a brisk lotion "exerciser" to stimulate circulation and to reawaken a lively young glow.

3. Spend a minute or two to help firm contours. Again with upward and outward motions, pat on a tightening semi-liquid over expression lines and on throat, chin, and jowls. Let it set. (See special directions for patting briskly with backs of hands under the chin and along the jaw line to help fight double chin and sagging muscles.)

4. Apply the richest emollient cream and moisturizer, one that works within the skin to replenish moisture and natural beautifying oils.

Many women past thirty-five use a hormone cream planned to replace the two female hormones that diminish with time—with a consequent loss of moisture and oils. This type of cream acts upon the skin to make it appear younger. At one time such creams were the subject of some controversy, but the use of female hormones (estrogens and progesterone) in skin care is now supported by scientific documentation. I have always been a believer in them and have used a hormone cream myself for more than thirty-five years. The current scientific findings make me believe that they will be the creams of the future for all women over thirty-five. But if you are not yet ready for a hormone cream, your most important step in postponing your skin's rendezvous with time is the nightly use of a rich emollient cream.

If you are beginning to worry about a double chin,

sagging jowls and throat, here is a routine to practice nightly following your make-up removal and skin treatment.

✔ Press chin forward as far as possible, then push lower lip forward. With chin and lip in same position, turn head very slowly to the right, then to the left. Repeat at least ten times.

✔ Stick out tongue and try to touch the tip of your nose. This strengthens throat muscles.

✔ Firm the jaw line by pretending you are chewing. Chew really hard and swing the mouth from side to side. Pretend you are trying to take a bite from an imaginary apple bobbing about in front of you. Open your mouth wide, then resisting as strongly as you can, slowly close it.

✔ Sleep without a pillow or allow yourself a flat one only. This wards off extra chins.

Seven Sins Against a Beautiful Complexion

1. *Not removing make-up properly.* It's a great temptation, when one is tired, to fall into bed without removing make-up. But it is asking for trouble. Stale make-up and the day's grime not only clog pores but eventually coarsen the skin. Really deep daily cleansing is a most important part of all skin care. Cleansing creams and lotions should be applied and reapplied until cotton or tissues come away clean. Always be sure your hands are spotlessly clean when touching your face.

2. *Using thick, heavy foundation.* This is another sure way of clogging pores. It's unattractive, too, for it is bound to "cake" during the day, especially in the deep lines around the nose and large pores near the chin. Today's foundations give a new glamorous finish, yet are light in texture.

3. *Treating your face roughly.* Use finger tips to apply make-up and cream in light upward and outward movements.

4. *Giving too little protection.* Every skin needs protection, and that means a moisturizer and foundation during the day. (For the outdoor girl it also means a sun

screen preparation and nightly skin treatment via a moisturizing cream.)

5. *Not getting enough fresh air.*
6. *Eating the wrong foods.*
7. *Going to bed too late too often.*

Once you have found the basic skin-care pattern that will be yours as long as your skin continues to act the same way, you leave a big beauty problem behind you. You can give up searching and make this basic skin care as much a part of your daily life as enjoying your morning tea or coffee. It is there to stay—unless, perhaps, your oily skin normalizes with time and treatment (as many skins do). Or your normal skin needs added moisture after forty. Or, by some accident of nerves or locale, you find yourself with a skin that shows its feelings too easily.

But beauty masks are different. They are like a vacation for your face, wonderful at any age when your skin needs a pickup. Especially after forty, I recommend that a mask be used regularly from twice to four times a week. But not any mask for any woman. I believe in the specialized mask for the particular skin.

For instance, a good mask for oily skin draws out tiny dirt specks, deposits of grease, clinging make-up particles. Masks for a quick pickup have a stronger action than "exercisers" or astringents. Some whip up circulation while others velvetize the skin. They're tonic to a tired face and give that little extra fillip to skin care.

Masks for Oily Skin, Blackheads

Are blackheads the bane of your existence? If so, about four times a week apply a *medicated beauty mask*. It only takes ten minutes and it helps to unclog pores. Cleanse your skin first, then spread a thin film of the mask on your face, applying it more lavishly where the blackheads congregate. Ten minutes later wash off with warm water. Surprised? I told you masks are marvels and your mirror will spell this out. Your skin looks smoother, more radiant.

Masks for Aging Skin

No woman ever wants to show her age. I have developed a mask containing herbals that works wonders on dry, crinkled skin. Have you a really important occasion ahead? By all means give yourself a twenty-minute session with this fragrant wonder. Weary skin seems to lose the tired down-droop as this *herbal mask* lifts and firms, temporarily erasing lines.

Another one of my favorites is an *invisible mask* for visible results—for every skin type. The most versatile mask ever, it contains certain natural extracts also found in one of my most famous creams. Lines seem to disappear. Your complexion suddenly looks smooth and transparent, and the unique advantage is that it is so light and flexible you needn't wash it away. You can let it stay on, invisible and light, uplifting under make-up.

Some skins crave stimulation. Now and then a sallow, sluggish skin cries out for a real rouser of a mask. And there is one that provides concentrated local stimulation with amazing smoothing. It is also a *herbal* formula and should be used twice a week and before special occasions to be sure of looking your best.

One of the most important things to remember in using a mask is to relax. Enjoy the time you spend giving yourself this treatment. Since you can't do too much else while the mask is on, why not use the time for a ten-to-twenty-minute rest. Saturate pads with a cool, refreshing lotion and lay them on your eyelids. Lie flat, elevate your feet, and allow your mind to go blank. The mask will do the rest.

A New View About Foundations

You treat your skin night and morning, but you should wear foundation make-up wherever you go. The right foundation continues to protect your skin. That's why I think of foundation (with the exception of its color content) as belonging primarily in the skin-care class. The right foundation continues to protect your skin hour after hour all day. In this era of sheer, natural-looking foundations which treat as well as color, any woman who is without one is depriving herself of one of the greatest beautifiers in existence.

Staying young and looking young means more than tidying up a wrinkle. It is knowing what is going on in beauty and taking advantage of the right thing for you. For instance: find a new foundation, the best you've ever known, and use it to its fullest potential.

WHY A FOUNDATION?

If you're one of the few women who dust their noses with a touch of powder and feel they've done all that's needed, you're most definitely missing something. The right foundation can do much more for you and you'll still look natural and delicate.

It will give your skin beautiful texture and more radiant color.

It will bring you and your clothes into closer harmony.

It will cover minor irregularities, tiny flaws and freckles.

Protect you against floating dirt in the city air and extremes in temperature.

Supplement your daily skin care with beneficial ingredients for your skin type.

And it will give a *finished, even* look to your skin available through no other means.

THE RIGHT FOUNDATION FOR YOU

Dry Skin? Your foundation should have the finest texture. It should be blended with softening substances so it can moisturize while it hides lines.

Oily skin? Your foundation should be lightly medicated to lap up oiliness and leave your skin matte-finished and dry.

Sensitive Skin? Your foundation should be velvet-smooth and gentle with special concealing coverage to block out flushing or uneven blotchiness.

Young Skin? Your foundation should be gentle. A cake foundation with milk protein does a perfect job without your having to use powder.

Blemished Skin? Your foundation should be medicated to help heal while it conceals. In a flattering shade it will easily solve many of your blemish problems.

DIRECTIONS FOR THE USE OF
BEAUTY PREPARATIONS

Don't clutter your thinking while planning a self-improvement course, but be sure to read the instructions issued with every product. Thanks to precise scientific facts, most good products come with detailed information on how to use them. The directions have been written with care. They explain the reasons for the product, the result you can expect, and how to use it most effectively. And many contain information on related preparations that can be helpful to you.

Once again, as a woman who has lived her life in the laboratories and the salons of beauty, I urge you—please read directions, follow instructions, and enjoy the beneficial effects of your beauty preparations.

3 What a Beauty Salon Can Mean to You

A BEAUTY salon should be used as your personal beauty information center. From the ground floor where treatment and make-up items are demonstrated and sold, to the upper floors where face, body, hand, and hair care are handled by trained experts, it is a source of advance beauty information.

There are body-massage rooms where the newest scientific treatments are given. There are facial rooms where you relax in reclining chairs with your feet raised while your face is cleansed, treated, massaged, masked and firmed. There are make-up rooms for group instruction and for individual corrective lessons. Many of the salons have steam rooms and baths, exercise areas and elaborate exercise equipment. Then there are the luxurious hairdressing salons where you can choose the latest hair fashions—or have your hair styled to your favorite coiffure.

But most important, in an atmosphere of calm and luxury there is a staff of informed people expert in helping you to help yourself. And many of us need help. We find it difficult going alone. Certainly one of the most important ingredients of a salon are these gifted humans with a flair for imparting confidence to women in need of beauty answers. I've always insisted the personnel in my salons have great insight and worldly knowledge. They are hand-picked, selected for their tact, pleasant manners, and understanding of human nature. Then, and only then, are they given months of training in all the complicated rituals of the beauty business. They must know what's right for their clients. Hence, when a woman enters a Helena Rubinstein salon anywhere in the world she is assured, as with my products, that quality comes first.

From the moment I opened my first salon in Australia I was aware that women were looking for more than mere technical directions or services. They wanted to breathe in a feeling of beauty in an atmosphere where their needs would be respected and cared for. So, over the years, my salons have been located in lovely, accessible buildings in the most fashionable parts of the great cities of the world. I have personally supervised the décor of the salons. I attempted to devise memorable color schemes, select comfortable furnishings, and I chose beautiful paintings from my own collection. In fact, I lavished the same affection and care on my salons as I did on my homes.

Because of this, women who visit the salons on a regular basis develop a sense of discrimination and appreciation. It is like visiting museums and recognizing the work of famous artists—knowing at a glance what is first-rate. That is why I feel so strongly that every woman who can should have at least one "salon experience." It will teach her much and give her knowledge about herself not available under any other circumstances.

For you who are close to my salons, it is my hope you will use them as they were intended—as a source of inspiration and knowledge. For those in places too remote to make this possible, perhaps you can create, in your own home, a small "place of your own" that has a salon atmosphere. It can be a carefully arranged dressing table—as simple as that—but it must be a place where charm and harmony nourish the spirit while you care for your beauty.

Salon Treatment

FOR DRY SKIN

Perhaps you'd like to know about a particular beauty treatment as it is given in all of the Helena Rubinstein salons. Here is a treatment for dry skin which is the most prevalent of all skin problems, especially with advancing years.

This treatment starts, as do all skin-care treatments, with a thorough cleansing. The skin is cream-cleansed and massaged at the same time. Our skilled operators work with the tips of their fingers, starting at the back of the neck, around to the throat, using both hands in lifting upward motions. Then to the face, lifting and massaging gently. The cleansing cream is tissued off with the same upward motions.

The second step is to awaken the circulation, to give a feeling of stimulation and bring fresh, natural color to the surface of the skin. A special stimulation lotion is applied and works on the skin as exercise does on the body—to help give it tone and firmness. It is pressed on gently but firmly and repeated over the expression lines a second and third time. Even the natural neck creases are not overlooked, for they can become deep, ugly lines if neglected.

Now the operator gives attention to the contours, to tighten relaxed areas. Puffiness under the eyes is gently fingerprinted with a tightening and firming preparation. The expression lines of the face, the jowls, and the chin get special attention—pat, pat, pat under the chin, with the backs of both hands. By the time this is completed every drop of the firming preparation has been completely absorbed by the skin.

The next step is often a mask treatment—the choice is based on individual skin tone. For a sallow skin a stimulating mask brings a lovely pink tone to the skin; for an overly pink skin a different type of mask is applied—always with both hands to give an upward lift. And while the mask does its work, eye pads saturated with a soothing, refreshing lotion are placed over the closed eyelids.

"Now relax," suggests the beauty operator, "or take a nap for the next twenty minutes if you like."

At the end of that time the mask is washed away. Lines seem to have fled . . . color is even . . . eyes are bright. A wonderful transformation!

There are various machines, too, which are very beneficial, and many clients return to the salon as much for the benefits of these beauty wonders as for any of the other treatments. Yes, beauty has also entered the machine age.

WHY THE SALON?

Besides the obvious beauty benefits, one of the most enjoyable features of salon treatments is that they are given in small, immaculate rooms painted in restful pastel colors. While the treatment is being administered you recline in a softly padded, adjustable chair so you can relax and enjoy a quiet rest. Each treatment is followed by a complete make-up created especially for you by an expert staff member, choosing the latest shades of foundation, lipstick, and eye shadow best suited for your coloring.

Why do I talk of salon treatment in detail when you are primarily concerned with doing things yourself? Simply to show you how you can create the same routines in your home, acting as your own beautician. You can use the same preparations. A salon beautician who gives you an initial treatment will be glad to explain, step by step, just what she is doing so that you can follow the routine yourself. That's why I feel at least one salon treatment is a very worth-while beauty lesson. Any observant woman can absorb the methods used by the operator and adapt them for her personal at-home beauty future.

CAN YOU HAVE A SALON AT HOME?

Of course you can, even in a limited space. There are many elements which can be easily duplicated at home. Try for the following during your "home-salon" moments:

A serene atmosphere of peace and tranquillity.

Something beautiful to look at—flowers, a painting, your favorite ceramic.

A chaise longue or a reclining chair or couch on which to relax fully during treatment time.

The preparations you need close at hand.

A pre-planned program of activities: basic skin care,

mask treatment, rest during treatment, hair setting and tinting, simple exercises, the ritual of the bath.

If you have an extra room or bathroom in your home, why not annex it for your beauty care. A playroom could be pressed into service, or a corner of your bedroom screened off and furnished with a large comfortable chair, a dressing table, and a full-length mirror.

I know of several of my clients who have expanded their bathrooms by installing a sunken tub and certain other fixtures that were never included in any standard bathroom—like a refrigerator to hold beauty preparations; some even have their own sauna bath. They have their own salons in miniature where there is space for a dressing table fitted with special lighting, a couch or chair covered in easily washable fabric or plastic, a professional hair dryer, and a variety of exercise equipment. One even has a rustproof exercise bicycle anchored in her shower. She pedals while the shower pours down on her, and she swears this water and exercise treatment is marvelous for her metabolism!

Having your own home beauty salon is entirely a matter of organization. Once you've decided on the space, gather all the equipment you need for treatments, skin care, and make-up in that one spot. Assemble the actual furnishings you need, keeping to bare essentials. Be sure the lighting is correct, there is a place to exercise and, ideally, have a washbasin and tub close at hand. With just a little additional space you might even emulate the client who has a small "beauty icebox" to keep creams and lotions cool in warm weather, to hold ice water and an inviting luncheon snack.

BEAUTY SUPPLIES FOR YOUR HOME SALON
Linens
- Clean sheets and blankets
- Pillowcases
- Towels and terry-cloth bathrobe
- Facecloths and tissues
- Washable, easy-to-slip-into smock or kimono
- Leotard, shorts, and a knitted top
- Washable rug to exercise on

Furnishings

✓ Large chair (comfortable and spacious) or a chaise longue

✓ Two pillows

✓ Full-length mirror

✓ Magnifying mirror

✓ Straight chair (for make-up purposes)

✓ Strong clear light

✓ Folding cot

✓ Slant board

✓ Radio or hi-fi set to relax by

Beauty Preparations

Your beauty preparations can be kept on separate trays or in those clear plastic boxes that serve so many purposes.

✓ Tissues, cotton, a water dish of unbreakable plastic.

✓ Hairpins, curlers, clips, etc., as well as combs, brushes, and hair preparations.

✓ Nail enamel in your favorite shades, hand cream, cuticle remover, and all the necessary manicure implements.

✓ Make-up for day and for evening, including all the items from foundation to eyebrow pencil.

A DAY OF BEAUTY AT HOME

✓ Prepare a light lunch that coincides with your diet requirements: lemonade or skim milk, a sliced tomato, green salad, a couple of hard-cooked eggs, a fresh fruit compote. Arrange them attractively and place them in the refrigerator until wanted.

✓ Do your exercises in front of a long mirror where there is space enough to spread a towel. Observe what you are doing.

✓ Give your hair a new tint or rinse.

✓ Set your hair. Change the style occasionally for fun and for the benefit of your scalp.

✓ Give your face a good cleansing followed by a special mask suited to your skin type.

✓ Then, with eye pads in place, stretch out on your bed while the mask does its work.

✓ Enjoy a luxurious bath with all the fragrant trimmings from bath oil to a good herbal body rub.

✓ Do your toes and fingernails.

✓ Stretch out for a fifteen-minute cat nap—but be sure to set your alarm. By this time you should be nicely relaxed.

✓ Eat your lunch.

✓ Slip into your underclothes and start to apply your make-up. Experiment with a few innovations borrowed from a current fashion magazine.

✓ If necessary, finish drying your hair with a hair dryer. Comb out your hair with care and spray it into place.

✓ Put on your dress, apply finishing touches to face and hair, then add accessories—jewelry, a flower, a bow —perfume yourself as is your habit.

✓ A day in your own home salon. Doesn't it feel wonderful? You'll feel so much better! You'll look so much prettier!

4 } Eat Your Way to Beauty

As we learn more about what food does *for* us and *to* us, I am more than ever convinced that what we eat today is what we are tomorrow. The well-informed dieter may eat with several purposes in mind—to achieve a trimmer figure and clearer skin or to have more energy or to sleep more soundly. I'm quite certain that as time goes by this aspect of dieting will be better understood.

Monotonous munching and crunching on a few deadly boring foods never helped anyone break away from bad food habits or overeating. It is more apt to induce thinking of salmon in aspic with green mayonnaise, or the Baked Alaska laced with rum so lovingly served at the old Vanderbilt Hotel in New York.

That's the reason I've always felt that dieting in conjunction with an over-all program of self-improvement is so much more satisfactory. One is not losing weight in a vacuum. Slimming while making oneself over is part of a whole brand-new effort to get into the swing of abundant living.

Diet is a way of eating for the kind of life you want. One day, in going over the reports from our exercise salon in New York, I noticed the name of a great Hollywood star. She was booked for three hours of exercise a day, with private instruction. I queried my exercise director.

"Isn't this a little strenuous?" I asked.

"She is used to it," responded Mme. Delclos. "She has been doing exercises for years and is as hard and trim as a race horse. Right now she has been promised an important part if she can lose twenty pounds in four weeks. There is no stopping her. She is living on lettuce, tomatoes, hard-boiled eggs and skimmed milk, with one-half slice of dry toast a day. She tells me every time she sits down to that egg, tomato, and lettuce she envisages her name in lights over the theater and she reads the lines from the play out loud to herself. Madame, she is fading away before our eyes. I couldn't do it, and I doubt if you could. She was slim to start with. She is not taking off easy-on, easy-off fat. She's taking off tissue. It takes three instructors to keep her going. Why does she come to us? She knows our exercises, but she says it's not so grim exercising when you have good company."

She got the part! *She was not just dieting. She was realizing her ambition as an actress.*

On another occasion I walked into the office of an advertising writer and glimpsed an apple cut in quarters on her desk. I asked her if she loved apples.

"Love them?" came the quick reply. "They've always annoyed me with all that built-in propaganda about keeping the doctor away. But this is my apple day. You see, Madame, I have a tendency to billow, and my doctor suggested that since I fail so miserably at following a steady diet, I try this stunt. Once a week I cut two apples into quarters. I eat a quarter every hour on the hour, drink oceans of water, and then go to bed early with a good book. The two apples equal about two hundred calories or a little over. I don't feel as though I'm really starving. The water cuts down my hunger, and going to bed early keeps me from eating a big dinner. This system reduces my weekly caloric intake tremendously."

Well, that's an interesting theory and it seemed to be working for this particular young lady. Actually she was weight-watching because she had the good judgment to know that, representing a firm involved in beauty, it would not stand her in good stead to blow up like a balloon.

She was not dieting. She was safeguarding her success.

One evening, at a dinner party in my home in Paris, I became aware that one of my guests had not touched his sweet dessert. It occurred to me that, like many Frenchmen, he might not be fond of sweet desserts and would prefer fruit and cheese.

"If you are in no mood for sweets tonight," I suggested, "it would be so simple to find you a dessert more to your taste."

"No, no," he replied. "With me it is not a choice between one dessert and another—but between pastry and people."

"Pastry and people?" I smiled.

"But yes," he explained. "I have observed lately that following an encounter with rich food I become drowsy. My eyes close. I am like a fat cat, ready to nap, not a good companion at all. So I have changed my way of eating. I like food, but I like companionship far more." So a great lover of wines and *haute cuisine* began to taper off his eating on behalf of his social existence. *He was not dieting. He was keeping his friends!*

Although I have been told that I appear somewhat taller, I am actually only four feet ten, with a tendency to gain weight in spite of rising at six in the morning and carrying on at an exhausting pace—for others, that is, not for me.

I became extremely conscious of diet and health when in my middle years I found myself nervous and utterly worn out. What was more worrisome, I was without the energy to carry on my work. Finally I became so ill my doctor sent me to the now famous Bircher-Benner clinic in Zurich. Here I learned that food—the right food— meant energy, and I was as earnest about recouping my energy as some women are about being able to wear a size twelve.

It was at that time that I began formulating the lifelong habit of starting the day with fruit juice and fresh fruit and including a generous variety of raw fruits and vegetables throughout the day. I began to appreciate proteins. *I was not dieting. I was holding on to vital energy!*

Through years of trying to help women help themselves to new figures and a new way of life, I have found there is a right way for everyone, and it can be achieved simply by sensible eating. But there is no magic formula. There are many different reasons why certain people put on weight and others lose it. Sorrow and fear may make one woman fat, another thin. Some women never get fat, yet others who eat the same foods and lead much the same life puff up. Nothing seems to be completely rational or logical where weight is concerned.

One doctor insists you must give up starches, while another tells you to be sure to include some. Alcohol is also controversial in diet. Some doctors are against it because it provides calories but no nutritive benefits; others claim that it helps by stepping up the metabolic rate.

The most recent sensation in diets is one which has been given various names ranging from the "Air Force" diet to the "Drinking Man's" diet. It is essentially one that severely limits your carbohydrate intake but is very generous with proteins and fats. It allows you to eat sufficiently so that temptation is your only problem—not hunger. There doesn't seem to be any doubt that it works for a great many people, but it does have its nutritional dangers. You should not embark on this diet or, for that matter, on any other one that radically changes your eating habits without consulting your doctor.

If a diet which is successful for someone else doesn't work for you, try another. Watch the results, weigh yourself every day, and eventually you will find the one that is best for you.

I am not a believer in crash diets taken on with abandon and then dropped in haste. Only too often they age the face and neck and damage the elasticity of the skin. And because they are too exacting and drastic, nobody seems to stay with them for any length of time. I recommend a way of eating that will, in time, establish new eating habits —habits that will stay with you. It may take a little longer to lose this way (if that's what you wish to accomplish), but weight once lost will never come back as long as you follow your new, purposeful eating habits.

My Own General Rules for Weight Control

✓ Make up your mind you're going to lose weight. Think of it as the most important job you have to accomplish.

✓ Don't *talk* about your diet. It bores others and soon it will bore you.

✓ Start each day with a glass of hot water into which has been squeezed the juice of one fresh lemon. No sugar.

✓ Eat bulky foods—spinach, cabbage, salad greens, and lean meat, so that you won't feel hungry.

✓ Before lunch and dinner drink a glass of cold water with the juice of half a lemon. It helps to overcome hunger. But don't drink while eating.

✓ Eat slowly. Chew your food thoroughly to aid digestion and to satisfy your appetite with less food.

✓ If you like milk, drink only skim milk. It's rich in proteins and free from fat.

✓ If you must have bread, eat very little, dark, rye, thin unbuttered toast.

✓ Keep salt off the table. And use it sparingly in the kitchen (preferably not at all).

✓ Never look at a menu. It's maddening.

✓ Don't think about rich foods. But if you crave a certain one, eat a tiny portion. Don't let a craving mount so that you eat a pint of ice cream when a tablespoonful would do.

✓ Begin breakfast with fresh fruit.

✓ Luncheon should be salad time—fresh fruit or raw vegetables and a simple dressing. Instead of tea or coffee drink skim milk.

✓ Hungry between meals? Have an apple section, a small piece of dry cheese, a celery or carrot stick, fresh orange juice.

✓ At dinner eat a small salad before the meat course. It cuts down the appetite. Limit bread and potatoes. Avoid fat rich foods.

✓ Leave the table while you still feel you could eat a little more.

✓ Prepare and serve your diet foods as attractively as possible, so that sensible eating becomes enjoyable.

If you have only a few pounds or a few inches to lose, keeping these rules in mind constantly and following them usually brings excellent results.

I've always been amused by the calorie counters who check religiously every item they're going to eat. They also give "scientific" dissertations on exactly what a calorie does—the measure of heat or energy it produces, and that if you eat more calories than you use, the excess food will be stored in the body as fat! Yet these same people who spend so much of their energies concentrating on calories often lose all point of contact with the purpose of diet and for this reason often fall by the diet wayside.

Better to be less accurate in your calorie counting—and more determined in maintaining a directional line to good looks and good health.

I feel that a little more understanding about food itself may go a long way toward helping you accomplish your new goals. These are very elementary facts. There is still so much to be learned—but a quick briefing will shed a candle glow of light on the matter of your diet. Pursue it further and you will find it can be an intensely interesting study, useful not only to yourself in weight control, but to your family and its healthful future.

Proteins build and repair tissue, tone muscles, help maintain the skin, and satisfy hunger. They are found in meat, fish, cheese, eggs, nuts, and dried vegetables like beans, peas, and lentils. Of these you should have lean red meat at least twice weekly. You can also have chicken, but not the fatty skin.

Fats generate heat in the body and produce fatty acids essential to life and to the lubrication of the skin. They are found in both animal and vegetable foods and especially in butter, oil, cheese, whole milk, and fat meats. These are foods you must use with restraint.

Carbohydrates, sugars and starches are consumed for energy, particularly muscular energy. They are plentiful in sugar, candy, pastries, sweets, bread, potatoes, rice, and flour, and in foods such as macaroni, spaghetti, noodles, all grain foods. If you are serious about slimming and trimming, you must be content with relatively small amounts

186

of these. Choose your sugars from unrefined sources such as fruits and honey.

Minerals. These special riches come from the earth and the sea. They are calcium, phosphorus, sodium, iodine, iron, and others. They are needed throughout the body for health. As an example, iron helps to keep the blood rich and red. Calcium is a bone builder, also needed for good teeth. Some of the foods which provide them are milk, meat, fish, fruit, and vegetables.

Vitamins serve specialized functions to the blood, skin, nerves, and all the body systems such as circulatory, glandular, digestive, etc. They are found abundantly in dairy foods, whole grain products, meat, poultry and fish, as well as vegetables, fruits and yeast.

During slimming diets, and due to overrefinement of foods, you will probably want to assist your diet with a balanced vitamin supplement.

Water is a necessity. We can survive only a few days without it. Water flushes the entire system . . . clears toxic materials. It exists in fruits, vegetables, meats, etc. To be at the peak of your energy and well-being you should also drink six glasses of water daily, but not at meals.

Roughage. A certain amount of roughage is vital for daily elimination; it provides bulk. Roughage exists in grain foods, cooked and raw vegetables, including salads. For keeping fit without fat, plan to derive your roughage from cooked and raw vegetables. Their bulk helps to curb eating.

The most important single thing to do in changing your eating habits is to decide *why* you want to change and *where* you are headed. You are a person about to take a trip that in itself may not be too interesting, but when you come to the end of the journey you will find a revelation! By all means focus on the reason for this activity . . . keep it clearly in front of you. Your destination may be finding restored energies so that every minute of life can be more meaningful. It may be that you have always wanted a clearer, smoother skin—now you will eat to have it. Or you may be entirely practical—with a closetful of gorgeous clothes, useless because they are too tight—too small. Your doctor may have warned you that too many pounds can be dangerous to your health . . . therefore eating wisely is essential. It is only by seeing the end or purpose of the diet clearly that you can remake your eating habits painlessly.

Talk it over with yourself . . . establish the motive now —not weeks from now! Begin to move toward the goal that *you* have set for yourself!

Eat Your Way to a Slim Figure

Eat less, much less. This is the essential direction for you to take. You must take in fewer calories than your body burns up in energy if you are to lose pounds. Overeating coupled with too little exercise makes for fat. It's very seldom (even if we'd like to think differently) that overweight is due to glandular malfunction.

You need foods which can maintain health at the lowest calorie count. And you will have to learn to like raw vegetables, salads and cooked green vegetables high in vitamins, low in calories. They also give you the bulk that reduces hunger and the roughage that aids elimination.

The following chart is your basic food pattern. The menus illustrate how to make these foods work together. They will start you off with a liquid day that will show real results quickly and make the following days of diet seem more than adequate.

GENERAL RULES
Undercook rather than overcook vegetables.
Broil or boil meat, chicken, or fish.
Eat slowly, chew well.
Cut down on salt.
Reduce hunger urges with a celery or carrot stick—or maybe an apple.
Keep your purpose in mind: remind yourself of it.

PLENTY OF THESE
VEGETABLES (cooked or raw): carrots, celery, cauliflower, artichokes, spinach, green beans, summer squash

SALADS: lettuce, endive, watercress, parsley, tomatoes, cucumber, escarole, radishes

MEAT: chicken, lean cuts of beef, veal, lamb, ham

FISH: lean fish such as flounder, sole, whitefish, halibut, cod; any shellfish; oysters, shrimps, clams, lobster, etc.

DAIRY PRODUCTS: American cheese, Swiss cheese

EGGS: a half dozen or so weekly—to replace meat or fish at a meal

FRUIT: oranges, grapefruit, strawberries, raspberries, apples, apricots, plums, cantaloupe, honeydew

BEVERAGES: tea, coffee (no sugar), water

FAT: butter (one pat daily), or oil (one teaspoonful daily)

A LITTLE OF THESE

VEGETABLES: peas, onions, winter squash

STARCHES: toasted whole wheat or rye bread, baked or boiled potatoes

FRUIT: pears, peaches, grapes

DAIRY PRODUCTS: American cheese, Swiss cheese

DRINKS: wine (the best is dry white wine)

FORGET THESE

VEGETABLES: dried beans, lentils, corn

STARCHES: bread, pastry, coffee cake, sweet rolls, pies, rice, spaghetti, macaroni

COLD CUTS: sausage, pâté de foie gras, liverwurst

FISH: herring, mackerel, tuna (packed in oil), salmon, sardines

MEAT: pork, goose, duck

DRINKS: alcoholic drinks, soft drinks (except diet varieties)

SWEETS: chocolates, candies, marmalade, jams, jellies

FAT: animal fat (except one pat of butter or one teaspoonful of oil daily)

Daily Menus for Weight Loss

If you need the discipline of a fixed menu to start you, here is a day-by-day plan for healthy weight loss. Drink some water between meals. Coffee or tea may be taken after meals, without cream and sugar. Sometimes when dining out it is not possible to follow this menu exactly.

Familiarity with your basic food pattern chart will help you use good judgment.

FIRST DAY
(Rest as much as possible today)
8 a.m.
8 oz. orange and lemon juice
11 a.m.
8 oz. vegetable juice
2 p.m.
1 cup consommé
5 p.m.
8 oz. mixed fruit juice
8 p.m.
1 cup consommé
11 p.m.
Yogurt or a glass of buttermilk, or if you'd rather, a glass of skim milk

THE FOLLOWING TWO WEEKS
On Rising
1 glass of hot lemon water (half a lemon to each glass of water)
Breakfast
Glass of skim milk
Black coffee or tea
Fresh fruit (no bananas) the equivalent of 4 oz., 1 medium apple, pear, or peach, orange, or half grapefruit
Lunch
2 boiled eggs
or
Hot vegetable plate (no potatoes, rice, or beans)
or
Fresh fruit salad with lemon juice
or
Mixed green salad with lemon juice or reducing dressing and a tablespoon of cottage cheese
2 Ry-Krisps
Dinner
Cup of consommé (optional)
Broiled meat (2 lamb chops or medium-size steak or veal cutlet)

190

1½ cups of cooked vegetables with small square of fresh
 butter
Fresh fruit, 4 oz. (an apple, orange, 2 plums, half grape-
 fruit, cantaloupe, or unsweetened strawberries)
 Bed Time
Yogurt or a glass of buttermilk

AFTER FIRST TWO WEEKS

To be followed until normal weight. When you are
halfway to your weight goal you may *sometimes* indulge
in a little extra (when you are invited out to dine), but
make up for it the next day.
 On Rising
1 glass of hot lemon water
 (half a lemon to a glass of water)
 Breakfast
Coffee or tea without sugar or cream
One slice of toast
One boiled egg (optional)
Fresh fruit (an apple, orange, half grapefruit, or 2 plums)
 not exceeding 4 oz.
 Lunch
2 boiled eggs
or
Hot vegetable plate
or
Fresh fruit salad with lemon juice or reducing dressing
 and a tablespoonful of cottage cheese
2 Ry-Krisps
 Dinner
Cup of consommé (optional)
Vegetable appetizer (preferably raw) with lemon juice or
 reducing dressing
Broiled or boiled meat (two lamb chops, a medium-sized
 steak, veal cutlet, chicken, or lean ham)
1½ cups of cooked vegetables with small square of butter
 (spinach, string beans, artichokes, endives, leeks,
 turnips, Brussels sprouts, cabbage, cauliflower, tomatoes, eggplant, onions)
4 oz. fresh fruit
 Bed Time
Yogurt, glass of buttermilk, or skim milk

Eat Your Way to a Clear, More Radiant Skin

Clear and radiant skin, you can be quite sure, is kept clean both outside and inside. Skins hampered by oiliness, blackheads, and blemishes need special help to control external and internal conditions. Your eating habits are of the essence. Guard against too many fats, starches, sugars. Stress your proteins, high-vitamin foods, and calcium. Dairy foods (not in excess) help provide calcium.

EAT

raw vegetables, salads (dressing should be lemon juice with *very* little oil)

lean meat, chicken or fish, broiled, boiled or roasted (without gravy)

boiled vegetables with a little fresh butter (added on the plate, not in cooking)

milk

cottage cheese

Swiss cheese

yogurt

buttermilk

whole-wheat or rye bread (preferably toasted)

fruit (raw or stewed) with little sugar

Jello

drink 6 to 8 glasses of water daily, between meals

AVOID

chocolate

pastry

cream

alcohol

soft drinks

pork (except lean ham)

sausage

fat

gravy

spices

fried food and stews

sea food

EAT WITH MODERATION

bread

starchy foods

eggs

coffee

tea

Heavy demands are made by business and by the social whirl. Energies fail; there isn't enough left to carry on with gusto. But you will discover that there is an almost inexhaustible supply of energy in the right foods, and these energy foods in many cases are slimming foods too. If you have felt tired and listless, with haunting anxieties and too little laughter, by all means try . . .

Eating Your Way to Energy

MONDAY

Breakfast

½ Grapefruit
2 slices whole-wheat bread and butter
Honey or marmalade
Coffee, tea, or milk
1 egg (optional)

Lunch

Grated raw carrots with lemon juice
2 slices of cold ham
Head of lettuce with oil and lemon
Stewed fruit

Small cup of coffee or glass of milk

Dinner

One cup of consommé
Two broiled lamb chops
Fresh string beans
1 boiled potato
1 yogurt
Small pastry

Bed Time

Glass of milk
1 apple

TUESDAY

Breakfast

Glass of orange juice
2 slices whole-wheat bread and butter
Honey or marmalade
Coffee, tea, or milk
1 egg (optional)

Lunch

Raw celery and radishes
Vegetable plate
Cottage cheese
Baked apple

Small cup of coffee or glass of milk

Dinner

One cup of vegetable soup
2 slices roast beef
Broccoli
Mashed potatoes
Stewed fruit

Bed Time

Yogurt
1 pear

WEDNESDAY

Breakfast

Glass of prune juice
2 slices whole-wheat bread and butter
Honey or marmalade
Coffee, tea, or milk
1 egg (optional)

Lunch

Small cup of coffee or glass of milk

Dinner

One cup of consommé
Broiled fish
1 boiled potato
Green salad

Grated raw cauliflower and
 lemon
2 scrambled eggs
Yogurt

Ice-cream
Small pastry
Bed Time
Glass of milk
1 apple

THURSDAY
Breakfast
½ grapefruit
2 slices whole-wheat bread
 and butter
Honey or marmalade
Coffee, tea, or milk
1 egg (optional)
Lunch
Grated raw carrot
Fruit plate
Cottage cheese

Small cup of coffee or glass
 of milk
Dinner
Cup of vegetable soup
½ broiled chicken
Fresh boiled cauliflower
1 baked potato
Stewed fruit
Bed Time
Yogurt
1 fruit

FRIDAY
Breakfast
Orange juice
2 slices whole-wheat bread
 and butter
Honey or marmalade
Coffee, tea or milk
1 egg (optional)
Lunch
Raw celery and radishes
Vegetable plate
Yogurt

Small cup of coffee
Dinner
1 cup consommé
Broiled steak or fish
Green peas
Mashed potatoes
Baked apple
Bed Time
Glass of milk
1 fruit

SATURDAY
Breakfast
Prune juice
2 slices whole-wheat bread
 and butter
Honey or marmalade
Coffee, tea, or milk
1 egg (optional)

Small pastry
Coffee or milk
Dinner
1 cup vegetable soup
2 broiled lamb chops
Lima beans

194

Lunch

Grated raw cauliflower and lemon

2 slices of ham

Head of lettuce with lemon

1 boiled potato

Stewed fruit

Bed Time

Yogurt

1 fruit

SUNDAY

Breakfast

½ grapefruit

Scrambled eggs and bacon

2 slices whole-wheat bread and butter

Honey or marmalade

1 egg (optional)

Coffee, tea, or milk

Lunch

Fruit cocktail

1 cup consommé

½ broiled chicken

Green peas, baked potato

Sherbet

Small pastry

Small cup of coffee

Dinner

2 slices of ham

Vegetable salad

Baked apple

Yogurt

Bed Time

Glass of milk

1 fruit

Have you found yourself tossing and turning? Do you start reliving the little annoyances of the day the moment you lie down to rest? Well, consider this interesting possibility—that the very foods you have been eating may be causing you to toss and fret. Wouldn't it be worth a good deal to recapture dreamless sleep? Here is a diet we recommend at the salon to non-sleepers. We think sleep is an important beauty ingredient. It freshens the skin, brightens the eyes . . . and prevents a taut, strained look.

Eating Your Way to Sleeping Soundly

The complete relaxation of sleep is one of the finest beauty treatments of all, and a full night's rest is the shortest cut to good looks, good health, and happiness. Nothing does more for your face, your figure, and your whole outlook on life.

For this diet I am giving seven alternative dishes for each meal, which will give you the opportunity to vary the menus as they fit in best with your own family routine.

195

Breakfast

Each day you may have:

2 cups of tea or coffee with milk (sweetened with a sugar substitute if you wish it).

1 heaped tablespoon of wheat germ with stewed prunes, stewed fruit, or grapefruit.

1 slice whole-grain bread (toasted or plain), lightly buttered or with honey.

For the main dish choose one of these:

    boiled egg

    poached egg

    scrambled egg

    grilled or broiled kipper

    haddock broiled in skim milk and water

    grilled lean bacon and tomato

    cold lean ham

Coffee Break

1 glass of skim milk (either hot or cold) into which you have stirred a tablespoon of powdered skim milk.

Lunch

This meal may be hot or cold, but make sure you have a mixed salad or a helping of a leafy green vegetable: turnip tops, spinach, kale. Brussels sprouts and the outer leaves of cabbage are rich in magnesium which combats fatigue and muscular tension.

For the main dish, choose one of these:

    grilled liver and bacon with tomato

    grilled kidney and lean bacon with tomato

    stewed chicken with mixed vegetables in casserole

    lean meat—roast beef, lamb or veal, steak, cutlets, or a chop

    roast chicken, turkey, pheasant (eat as little of the skin as you can)

    grilled halibut or cod

    white fish (grilled or broiled)

(If you like a potato with this meal, eat it boiled or baked in its jacket to make sure you get all the valuable vitamins and minerals.)

Tea

Two cups of tea, with lemon or with a little milk, but no sugar (artificial sweetening is permissible).

Dinner

With this meal you should have either a green salad or a green or yellow vegetable, making your choice according to what you have eaten at midday, and some fresh fruit, preferably citrus or an apple.

For the main dish choose one of these:

cheese omelet

poached egg with cheese sauce

cauliflower, Brussels sprouts, or carrots au gratin

tomato and onion pie

finnan haddie and tomato

cod casserole

egg salad

Cheese makes an excellent finish to this meal and/or the midday meal.

Midday and evening meals are interchangeable; the important thing is to ensure that every day you eat enough of those foods which you need.

If you have ever had the experience of finding an old familiar task difficult . . . unable to organize your thoughts . . . feel a bit detached and find it hard to come down to earth . . . don't worry, you're really not losing your mind. You may be suffering from a mild case of nervous exhaustion—many people do suffer this way without realizing their problem. But you can recapture much of that zing and zest, simply by a shift of emphasis in diet. The foods you eat may be slowing you down. Many people are absolutely astounded by what a week of this kind of dieting can do for them. Not only does it trim them down —it also seems to speed up their thinking!

Do-Your-Job-Better Diet

On Waking

The juice of one fresh lemon in a glass of hot water is the first step in the day.

In place of lemon and water, if you have any spots or blemishes on your face, chest, or back, cover 2 oz. prune purée with fresh lemon juice. Leave overnight beside your bed. Drink when you wake. Follow, half

197

an hour later, with a glass of hot water. Do this every day for one month, then three times a week for a further four weeks.

Breakfast

Whole grain cereal (hot or cold) with fresh or stewed fruit
1 egg (boiled or poached) *or* lean bacon (grilled, not fried) with tomatoes *or* fish (herring, mackerel, kipper, haddock, sole, trout)
1 slice whole-grain toast (or bread), lightly buttered
Coffee or tea with milk but no sugar

Lunch

Large glass of tomato juice
Cup of clear soup or bouillon
Large health salad
Stewed fruit with yogurt *or* fruit jelly *or* small piece of cheese

Dinner

Clear soup or bouillon or melon or grapefruit
Fish such as halibut, cod, sole, *or* poultry,
    game, *or* lean meat, calf's liver, kidneys, or sweetbreads
1 green leafy vegetable and 1 yellow vegetable such as carrots or turnips and 1 medium potato boiled or baked in jacket
Stewed fruit or fresh fruit

A woman who is thin generally crows with delight that she is nothing but beautiful bones, while her friends are making such valiant efforts to slim down. But there is a point where slenderness becomes plain skinniness—and good bones become sharp slats. When the realization strikes home that you are much too thin, and all is not well, or if you've been losing for no apparent reason—by all means have a chat with your doctor. Before you start dieting your way back to curves, be sure there isn't some hidden cause of weight loss other than worry, tension, or a certain feverish, driving pitch that seems to strip the frame of its cushioning fat. Your doctor may have very definite notions of what is happening. By all means let him help.

And in the meantime, please take these suggestions and this diet to heart.

Eat Your Way Toward a Fuller, More Curvaceous Figure

Rules for Gaining Weight

✓ Relax for ten minutes before lunch and before dinner.

✓ Drink from 6 to 8 glasses of water every day.

✓ Eat slowly; chew your food thoroughly.

✓ Eat an ample breakfast, and do not rush with it.

✓ Try to take a leisurely, pleasant walk outdoors every day, preferably in the sunshine.

✓ Exercise ten minutes a day in a slow and easy rhythm.

✓ Sleep nine hours whenever possible. Rest quietly for a short time after lunch and dinner.

✓ Relax whenever you have a chance; don't rush from one thing to another.

✓ Do not smoke excessively or before meals.

✓ Dress warmly in cold weather.

✓ If you are nervous, fretful or worrisome, try to overcome it, for this often causes loss of weight.

✓ It is most important to have good elimination.

NOTE: Take a glass of milk mid-morning, mid-afternoon, and at bed time.

MONDAY

Breakfast

1 glass orange juice (8 oz.)

¾ cup cooked Cream of Wheat

2 slices buttered rye or whole-wheat toast

tea or coffee with cream and sugar

Lunch

2-egg omelet

mixed green salad with 2 tbsp. French dressing

2 slices buttered whole-wheat toast
1 slice fresh pineapple
tea or coffee with cream and sugar

Dinner
hearts of celery and radishes
1 cup cream soup
1 portion roast beef
1 medium-sized baked potato
1 serving fresh peas
1 slice buttered bread
1 portion apple pie
tea or coffee with cream and sugar

TUESDAY
Breakfast
½ large grapefruit
2 strips of bacon
1 poached egg
2 slices buttered whole-wheat toast
tea or coffee with cream and sugar

Lunch
1 large fresh fruit salad with French dressing
2 slices buttered whole-wheat bread
1 cup custard
tea or coffee with cream and sugar

Dinner
hearts of lettuce with Russian dressing
1 cup consommé with noodles
broiled halibut
1 portion fresh lima beans
1 portion beets
1 slice buttered bread
1 portion tapioca pudding
tea or coffee with cream and sugar

WEDNESDAY
Breakfast
1 dish sweetened stewed rhubarb
1 portion corn flakes

200

2 slices buttered whole-wheat toast
tea or coffee with cream and sugar

Lunch
1 fresh vegetable plate with poached egg
1 square of butter for vegetables
2 slices buttered rye bread
1 dish of strawberries with cream and sugar
tea or coffee with cream and sugar

Dinner
1 cup tomato bouillon
1 portion calf's liver
2 strips crisp bacon
1 portion fresh asparagus with Hollandaise sauce
1 portion of squash
1 slice buttered bread
1 piece of cake
tea or coffee with cream and sugar

THURSDAY
Breakfast
1 glass of grapefruit juice (8 oz.)
2 eggs scrambled with milk and butter
tea or coffee with cream and sugar

Lunch
1 cup of clear soup
1 fresh vegetable salad with mayonnaise
2 bran muffins, buttered
1 glass whole milk
1 piece of pie

Dinner
1 fresh fruit cup
2 slices baked ham
1 small baked sweet potato
1 portion spinach
1 slice of buttered bread
1 piece of chocolate cake
tea or coffee with cream and sugar

FRIDAY
Breakfast
1 glass prune juice
1 dish oatmeal
1 soft-boiled egg
2 slices buttered rye toast
tea or coffee with cream and sugar

Lunch
cream soup
vegetable salad and mayonnaise
2 medium-sized buttered rolls
1 baked apple with heavy cream

Dinner
1 cup clam chowder with crackers
1 portion boiled salmon with egg sauce
1 portion fresh string beans
1 portion stewed tomatoes
1 slice of buttered rye bread
1 piece of layer cake
tea or coffee with cream and sugar

SATURDAY
Breakfast
1 dish apple sauce
4 strips bacon
2 slices buttered whole-wheat toast
tea or coffee with cream and sugar

Lunch
1 portion of cheese soufflé
1 small tomato salad with French dressing
2 slices of buttered whole-wheat bread
tea or coffee with cream and sugar
1 bunch of grapes

Dinner
carrot fingers and celery hearts
1 portion cream soup
1 portion broiled chopped steak
1 portion new cabbage

1 portion au gratin potato
1 slice buttered rye bread
1 fresh fruit cup
2 cookies
tea or coffee with cream and sugar

Sunday
Breakfast

½ grapefruit
2-egg omelet with ¼ cup minced ham
2 slices buttered whole-wheat toast
tea or coffee with cream and sugar

Lunch

tomato salad and mayonnaise
½ broiled chicken
1 boiled medium-sized potato with 1 square melted butter
    and chopped parsley
1 portion cauliflower
1 buttered roll
1 small portion of ice cream
1 cookie
tea or coffee with cream and sugar

Dinner

Mixed green salad with French dressing, 4 or 5 shrimps
    and cream cheese
3 Ry-Krisps, buttered
1 dish stewed fruit
2 cookies
tea or coffee with cream and sugar

5 Delightful New Ways to Exercise

IT is hard even for me to believe that when I opened my first salon in London, women actually entered it by the side door lest they cause a scandal! Today we are living in an age of sophisticated beauty care, and nowhere is this more apparent than in the area of exercise. Exercise stimulates the circulation, helps to eliminate poisons, brightens the skin, and gives muscle tone. It helps keep weight under control so that you can be proud of your figure.

Is it because all these benefits are as free as air that they are not valued as highly as they should be? I think failure to exercise is largely due to laziness. It may seem difficult to fit exercise into the everyday routine, but if you are really determined you will manage to find a few moments each day for stretching and bending exercises, raising your arms high while you inhale deeply—and you will look and feel all the better for it.

Let me tell you a story. One summer, some years ago, I was vacationing in Switzerland. Each morning I rose early for a brisk walk in the exhilarating, clover-fragrant air. The mountain tops were still covered with snow, the sky was cloudless, and I could hear the cowbells tinkle as the herds moved along the Alps. Switzerland in summer is deliciously fresh. Walking ahead of me every day I saw a tall, slim, white-haired woman. Her walk was as free and swinging as a sixteen-year-old girl's and her carriage was equally impressive. Imagine my delight one day, when asked to make a foursome at bridge, to find that my partner was none other than the white-haired walker who strode before me each morning. I was surprised to learn that she was well over seventy. I continued to chat with her many times during my holiday and finally one morning, when I felt she no longer thought of me as a stranger, I said, "Madame, as you know, my life has been spent helping to beautify women. May I tell you, you have a superlative walk! How did you accomplish it? How do you maintain it?"

"You make me very happy," she answered, "with your lovely compliment. Really, there is nothing to it. I stay supple by doing stretching exercises five minutes each morning before I get out of bed. I've done this for over fifty years. Then I go for a brisk walk while my body is still limbered up."

She had found the ideal way of making exercise a part of her everyday life. Why don't you? Then you will walk like a young girl even at seventy! However busy your life may be, there are moments during the day when your body is free to exercise—even though your mind may be occupied with other things.

Here are your exercises in bed—and on rising

1. Before you rise, lying flat on your bed, stretch one heel, then the other, toward the foot of the bed. Now raise first one leg, then the other. Lower one leg, then the other, slowly. (As your legs grow stronger you can lower them both together.) As you raise the legs, breathe in; as you lower them, breathe out.

2. Now stretch your arms back over your head as far as you can reach. Bring them back again until they are raised at right angles to the body, and stretch—with the tips of your fingers pointing to the ceiling. Relax. Breathe in on the reach; breathe out on the relax. Repeat ten times.

3. Rise, stand with feet together, and bend slowly, knees straight, until your fingers touch the floor. If you cannot quite touch the floor at first, don't give up. Reach as far as you can, ten times daily, and before long you'll be supple enough to do this exercise without effort.

4. Now stand tall, breathe deeply, and reach toward the ceiling. Lower your arms to your sides. Breathe in through the nose on the rise—out through the mouth when the arms are lowered. Repeat ten times.

You can also exercise in the tub . . . I do

It's a wonderful place to do facial exercises, hand and foot exercises (see "Fingertips and Toetips"), while making the most of your morning bath. Exercises done in water always seem so much easier. You float through them. I only wish that I could bathe in a swimming pool, as the Romans did. There is no better exercise in the world than swimming. If you have a tendency to stiffen, doing exercises in your tub will limber you up and help free the joints of stiffness. This is particularly effective for the older person with failing energies.

Exercise refreshes you

The ideal time to exercise in the evening is when you return from work at about 6:00 o'clock. You're tired after a busy day. Exercise is the best pick-me-up in the world, especially when you couple it with deep breathing —always inhaling on the lifting motions and exhaling on the downward sweep. You come home, exercise, take a brisk, swift shower, rest for five or ten minutes flat on your back, and then quickly slip into fresh clothes for an evening of relaxation or amusement.

Choose the Exercises That Are Best for You

The following exercises represent a very selective group, used in my salons. Concentrate on the ones that will solve your special problems. And remember—exercising in front of a mirror is remarkably helpful.

For posture and balance

Stand four inches away from wall. Using an exercising aid of elasticized rope with looped handles, slip hands into loops. Pull abdomen in so that small of back touches wall. Press pelvis forward and relax knees. Holding rope taut, raise arms above head. Keeping this position, bend body to right, then to left, keeping arms and body close to wall. Repeat five to ten times.

For the derrière and hips

Sit on floor with feet together, knees straight. Holding elasticized rope overhead, "fanny walk" along the floor, rolling one hip after the other. Shoulders should be in a straight line always. "Walk" back in the same position. Ten rolls in both directions, ten times.

For the chest, throatline and upper arms

Slip hands into loops of elasticized rope. Slip it back over your shoulders, letting it rest on shoulder blades. Now, keeping elbows straight, extend arms to shoulder level and bring palms together. Separate hands slowly until arms are at wingspread position, thrusting chin out. Bring palms together and repeat.

For the waistline and flanks

Slip hands into loops of elasticized rope. Stretch arms overhead and out to the full length of rope. Now, holding line taut, swing your torso from side to side.

For the tummy, hips and waistline

Loop elasticized rope securely over each instep. Lie down flat with toes pointing up toward ceiling. Now, grasping center of rope with both hands, pull against it to bring yourself to a sitting position. Lie down and repeat.

For the upper legs and calves

Loop elasticized rope over each instep. Lying flat on floor, with toes pointing upward, grasp rope firmly in center with both hands. Keeping torso on floor, bring legs straight up and slowly lower them without bending knees.

For the thighs

Loop elasticized rope over ankles. Lie on floor, arms outstretched at shoulder level, knees bent, feet on floor. Straighten legs and stretch them to ceiling. Now open legs

What a good time for all the good things of a Kent.

**Mild, smooth taste.
King size or Deluxe 100's.
Exclusive Micronite® filter.**

What a good time for all the good things of a Kent.

Warning: The Surgeon General Has Determined That Cigarette Smoking Is Dangerous to Your Health

Letter 'n Kent!

wide to full extent of rope. Close legs, bend knees and bring feet to the floor.

EXERCISES FOR FIGURE IMPROVEMENT

The hips and thighs
Lie on back on the floor, with arms and legs wide apart. Swing right leg over to the left side as far as you can, then slowly bring the leg back to a wide-open position flat on the floor. Alternate with the left leg. Repeat ten times.

The waistline and hips
Lie back on the floor with arms overhead, holding elasticized rope wide. Bend knees to the chest and, holding both legs together, roll hips to one side. Keeping arms flat on the floor, roll back and over on the other side. Repeat ten times.

The stomach
Lie on back on the floor, arms outstretched at shoulder level. Lift both legs, toes pointing toward ceiling, legs straight. Move legs toward and away from body. Repeat ten times at first. Increase when you can.

The legs and knees
Hold on to back of chair, standing close and keeping back straight. Do a knee bend and bounce one, two, three times in knee-bent position. Stand up, keeping back straight. Repeat five to ten times.

The upper arms
Lie on back on the floor, legs straight, arms overhead on floor, holding elasticized rope folded once and then over again. Lift arms quickly toward ceiling. Bring arms back to floor as slowly as possible, arms straight throughout. Repeat thirty times.

The neck
Lie on back on the floor, arms stretched out at shoulder level, palms turned up. Lift head and shoulders and pull chin toward chest, keeping hands on floor. Relax slowly. Repeat ten times.

All-over circulation
Sit on floor, legs wide apart. Place left hand on floor next to left hip. Lift right arm and right hip and stretch to the left, turning hip. Pull as hard as you can from toe

to fingertips. Alternate to the other side. Do this ten times on each side.

EXERCISES FOR RELEASE OF TENSION

Tension is a problem in modern life when every woman is expected to be a cook, chauffeur, mother and glamorous career woman rolled into one. Try these exercises to help release tensions.

For tense feet

Toe left. Standing with feet flat on floor, raise toes while keeping balls of feet on floor.

Roll out. Standing with feet on floor and parallel, roll feet to outer sides, then curl toes under.

Heel cord stretch. Keep heels flat on floor, in standing position, while bending knees as far as possible. (From constant wearing of high heels, cord becomes shortened.)

For tense or tired legs, and general fatigue

Sit with legs crossed and let the upper part of the body drop forward. Relax completely.

Slide hips forward in chair. With knees straight, extend legs forward as far as possible, toes reaching toward the ceiling, heels on the floor—and feel the pull! At the same time stretch the muscles of the back upward.

Sit in armchair, with hands on arms of chair. Bring one knee up as close to the nose as possible, toes pointing upward, heels down.

For headache, neck and shoulder tension

Relax in chair, turn head slowly as far to the right as it will go, then forward and down, and over to the left. Repeat. Reverse, turning head first to the left, then *backward,* and over to the right. (This should be done slowly to get the fullest benefit.)

Sitting erect, lean forward from hips with arms stretched forward. Raise arms high overhead, pressing shoulders back. Open arms wide and lower them to place hands in back of chair. Clasp hands behind, lift head and try to bring elbows together.

Press shoulders down, lift chin up, extend out and slowly bring chin down close to chest. Lift chin and repeat.

210

Raise arms and stretch up—up; then place hands on back of neck and massage neck and shoulders.

FRENCH FACIAL GYMNASTICS

From my Paris salon come these new and specific exercises for face, chin and neck.

For chin, neck and jaw

Open mouth and thrust lower jaw in and out as far as possible. Keep shoulders straight and head straight on neck. Move jaw from side to side as far as it will go.

Keep back straight; rotate head on neck, being careful not to drop head too far forward. Rotate in a complete circle, first to the left, then to the right. (This exercise is also excellent for the "dowager's hump.")

Cheek and expression lines

Press the three middle fingers of each hand underneath the cheekbones. Against the pressure of the fingers smile in a forced manner. Smile and relax. (This exercise helps drooping expression lines and jowls.)

Eyes

Keeping the eyes closed, blink hard, contracting the muscles around the eyes. (This is excellent for puffiness under the eyes, drooping eyelids, and eyebrow arch.)

Forehead

Make a half-circle of your thumbs and forefingers on your head above the hairline with your forefingers touching. Push back scalp and relax to normal position.

Today many occupations are sedentary. We deal with ideas. We have few occasions to really use many parts of our bodies. And how the body suffers! It goes limp and flabby, becomes unresponsive. There is nothing quite as expressionless as a body incapable of easy, light motion. By accepting the fact that to move well one must keep moving, you can retain grace and beauty for the rest of your life.

Fit exercise into your life.

Walk and walk more . . . and you will be fit for happy living!

6 ∮ A Hundred Faces for One

MAKE-UP is a child of the times and the darling of fashion. You can find a basic skin care and live with it forever, with a few minor changes, but the woman who lives with the same make-up techniques and the same make-up shades soon becomes dated, her beauty a little passé.

There will always be an "in" look and an "out" look. Your elegance depends on your unerring judgment about which is which. The face you turn to the world must be the face of your own times—and your most interesting assignment will be to discover it, sense it while it is still new and adapt *what is right for you* from fashion's face.

The "look" in make-up is always related to the seasonal swing of fashion. If it is a time of casual designs and freedom in dress, the make-up edict may be to glow with health, for the two seem to have an affinity. If clothes move in the direction of soft femininity and there is a return of the ruffle and dressmaker detail, if elegance is the underlying theme, then the "look" is likely to be pale and luminous!

But as mouths go pale, dark, bright, and then pale again

—from all those pales you will choose *the* pale that makes your eyes sing, *the* bright that lends added luminosity to your skin, *the* dark that glows against your skin like a jewel.

And remember this—with make-up you can be a woman of a hundred faces. The color mood is seasonal; it shifts from winter into summer. And every woman knows that the face which shops by day is quite different from the one that dances at night.

If my abiding passion has first been the care of skin, it is because I know to what extent make-up can be used to embellish a basically beautiful skin—not to coat and cover, but to reveal and accent this choice possession.

What can make-up do for you? It can transform an ordinary skin into a beautiful one—add luster and radiance to a fine skin, conceal minor imperfections. It can also modify the size and shape of your features and enhance your eyes. It can, in fact, work miracles.

Rules for Applying Make-up

Always make up in a good light, and study the final effect in a magnifying mirror near an uncurtained window.

At night use the same mirror under a strong artificial light.

Know what you are about to do, then do it. Hand and eye become precise with practice.

Take your time. Be careful with make-up.

Adopt those modern tricks that make eyes seem sparkling and disguise signs of fatigue and less than perfect features.

Use plenty of fresh cotton to remove excess powder.

Details are important. Watch them.

Work lightly.

Apply Your Make-up in This Order

1. Moisturizer
2. Foundation
3. Contour Correctives
4. Rouge
5. Face Powder
6. Eye Make-up
7. Lipstick

MOISTURIZER

Dot your moisturizer over the entire face. If your complexion is very dry, let it soak in, then reapply. Watch dry skin areas around the eyes, mouth corners, and forehead.

FOUNDATION

Lightly, lightly now dot your foundation on nose, cheeks, and chin as well as at the base of the neck. With upward motion, smooth all over the face and neck, around to the back of the neck and up under the chin. Include eyelids, and smooth the foundation up under the eyes right to the lower lashes, blending lightly. Blot up excess with tissue held against your skin—don't wipe! Tiny veins or blemishes can be concealed by a light second coat. Foundation, as you know, protects your skin; it gives first aid to a difficult one and brings color to a sallow complexion. Its tone should enhance the natural skin tone.

Although no two skin tones are alike, every skin falls into one of three color groups:

The neutral—from white to olive.

The pink—from light blush to deep rose.

The golden—from creamy ivory to sunlit bronze.

Your choice of foundation

It is best to try the color of a foundation on the inside of your arm, at the elbow. The skin here is not as much exposed to light, and you can see the effect more easily. Your foundation should not be more than one shade darker or lighter than your basic skin tone. It should make your entire complexion tone smooth and consistent and serve as a clinging background for the rest of your make-up.

There are many kinds of foundations. Each has been purposely designed for a special skin type, and it's important to select the one that does most for you.

Foundations come in a great variety of shades. It is usually wiser, however, not to move too far away from the shade that Nature gave your skin in the first place. But if you plan to do any corrective modeling of features with foundation, you must have a lighter and a darker shade —and not just one shade apart. Two shades apart is more effective for this purpose.

A covering fluid has powder in the fluid itself as well as moisturizing elements to preserve the skin's dewiness. It comes in a full range of shades.

Liquid cream foundation with an emollient base is especially good for those with normal to dry skin. It is kind to all except excessively oily skins.

Solid cream foundation is non-drying and opaque and is recommended when there are broken veins and under-skin blemishes.

Untinted cream foundation is one that every woman should have for certain occasions. It looks fresh and natural and can be used to cover and protect the natural complexion. It also has a powder-holding quality.

Medicated foundation is essential for an acne-blemished skin. It heals while it conceals.

Sun lotion, containing moisturizing elements as well, is also used as a protective foundation for sensitive skins by people who plan to spend a good deal of time outdoors.

All-in-one make-up foundation and powder is excellent for almost all types of skins. It gives a smooth surface with a lovely transparent effect.

When applying your foundation be sure to blend in all over face and neck. (And with a low-cut gown don't overlook your shoulders, upper back, and chest.)

CONTOUR MAKE-UP

For those who are not familiar with contour make-up, it's based on a very simple principle—light colors bring the features forward, dark colors move them back. You

216

can actually model with light and shadow. Just as a photographer retouches a photograph, you can retouch your face with color to minimize imperfect features and emphasize good ones.

Jawline a little heavy. Blend a touch of lighter-than-normal foundation under the eyes and work it out toward the temples. In that way you broaden the upper part of the face ever so slightly, and the jawline "seems" narrower by contrast. You can diminish the jaw further by shadowing with one light stroke of darker than normal foundation smoothed in with the fingertips.

Nose too broad. A stroke of deeper tone foundation down the sides will make it look narrower. A highlight brushed down the center of the nose with a single-stroke of lighter-than-normal foundation gives even more delicacy.

Nose too long or too pointed. Round off with a touch of darker-than-normal foundation blended in smoothly.

Receding chin comes forward when highlighted with a touch of white lipstick or foundation fingertip blended.

Double chin. Shadow it with a deeper foundation under the chin, blending up over the jaw.

Broad cheeks. Hollow them by shadowing with brush-on color below the cheekbones.

Face too wide. Brush side planes with color from temple to jaw.

Lines from nose to mouth. Use pale foundation over the lines; blend edges into your normal foundation. Leave and dust over with face powder.

In no time at all you'll be using both foundation and powders to model the face of your fancy . . . and to enhance the one you have.

ROUGE AND "BLUSHERS"

Rouge can be had in several forms, liquid, cream, or cake. Liquid rouge is the most delicate; cream rouge is easiest to control; cake rouge is good for quick touch-ups between make-ups. Liquid and cream rouge are used with liquid and creamy foundations, cake rouge with powder. Then there are the new "blush" powders. They are used to brush on an over-all glow, as well as to "contour" the face.

To use cream or liquid rouge, put a speck in the palm of your hand and blend with a tiny dot of foundation. Then finger dot under the eyes, below the center of the eye; put one dot further down on each cheek, slightly higher than the tip of the nose, and one below the corner of the eye. Blend these dots up and out toward the temples so there is no beginning and no ending. A fluff of color is your aim, not a flash! By using too much you detract from your eyes.

Narrow face? Place the dots farther apart.

Broad face? Narrow the distance between dots.

Long face? Blend color wider on the cheeks.

Rouge against time and fatigue

If your face looks tired, drawn, slightly weary, dot a little rouge *lightly* on your forehead and down the sides of forehead and temples. Now blend the color into your forehead and down the sides of the face toward the corners of the eyes, to meet the natural high spot of color on the cheeks, then out toward the hairline. The result is a healthy glowing look even though you're feeling exhausted.

Rouge and your eyes

If there are laugh lines at the corners of your eyes, bring your rouge up toward the outer corners of the eyes—right to the eyes, but *lightly*. This is diverting. People see color, not lines!

Rouge and your nose

Does your nose tend to turn pink in the cold? Try a lighter covering foundation at the tip, powder over it *and* tip your chin with a little cream or dry rouge. Since nose and chin both look pinky, your nose will stand out less.

Rouge and your ears

Do you wear your hair in an up-sweep? Rouge your earlobes, by all means. Illness or too much dieting can sometimes make earlobes pale and waxy looking, which suggests ill health. A touch of pink and you're not only glowing but your earrings, should you wear them, will be more dramatic.

Rouge and foundation

Everyone has a pale day now and then. "Blushers" or

a little creamy pink rouge blended into a beige foundation and applied lightly over the entire face is like wearing sunshine. But be careful . . . a light hand is needed here if you don't want a hectic flush.

FACE POWDER

This is one of the oldest, time-tested means of beautifying a woman's face. Yet how powder has changed and improved in my lifetime! I never cease to be amazed at the quantity of subtle shades that exist today. How fine and delicate texture has become! How subtle the colors!

How to use face powder

If you use a foundation which contains face powder, there are times when you will prefer not to use powder at all. But when you *do* use it, use it abundantly. Always on a clean puff or pad of cotton. Dip your puff deep into your powder and press it generously on the face—all over the face—forehead, eyes, cheeks, chin, nose, and throat. Let your powder set while you put on your eye make-up. Then with fresh cotton and soft downstrokes remove the excess powder, flattening any little hairs on the sides of the cheeks that might catch the light.

How to choose your face powder

Pick a powder shade slightly darker than your own natural skin tone. It will work up lighter. If you are pale or sallow, select a shade with an undertone of peach or pink. If you are inclined toward a florid tone, a pale shade of powder will work wonders. Sometimes the pallor that goes with age is best counteracted by a deep-toned powder, but be careful of this, as dark powders tend to cake at the nostrils.

Fantasy and face powder

Face powders can be used to create the most amazingly subtle effects. Work with them, study them, try using one over the other, a light shade dusted over a darker shade, for instance. Or try a light powder over a creamy foundation for an effect of velvety depth. Only you can decide how to mix your powders to suit your own skin and your own personality.

EYES SHOULD BE MAGNIFICENT

Eyes speak eloquently—they reach out to make friends for you. They express your feelings. Eyes should be beautiful—and today they can be *magnificent* because there are so many new techniques and remarkable preparations to bring their beauty out of hiding.

Eye Shadow Is a Great Ally

It comes in dewy soft colors and dark definitive ones —in cream, liquid or powder, and each with special merits. Used with discretion and a steady hand, eye shadow will make your eyes look larger, enhance their color, and add that certain allure that transforms the open-book gaze into one of mystery and appeal.

HOW TO APPLY EYE SHADOW

Over your powder which covers the entire upper eyelid, draw or blend on the eye shadow color of your choice—from the center of the lid up and out, toward the tip of the eyebrow. Try to keep the color light and blend to almost nothing at the edges of the upper sweep. Then fluff on a little face powder over the shadow to "fix" the color.

EYE SHADOW SUGGESTIONS

Colors may be chosen to match the eye itself, but I prefer contrast. It brings out color with no attempt at matching. Why not try the subtlety of a mauve shadow with gray eyes . . . brown shadow with green eyes . . . violet with blue eyes. This hint of color on the lids calls attention to the eyes themselves. You can harmonize, complement, or contrast eye shadow with your costume, even using a special shade to repeat a costume color. Or occasionally you might use two shades, blending one into the other.

EYE SHADOW PLACEMENT

The art of using eye shadow lies in the way you place it, where its deepest value is felt. Here are a few rules made to be broken.

Larger eyes. To create this effect place eye shadow at center of the upper lid and blend out to the brow tip.

Shallow eyes. To correct this, place eye shadow over center of upper lid, using a deeper tone of color just below the brow.

Older eyes. To disguise, be sure to keep eye shadow above the crease of the eyelid, closer to the brow.

Squinty eyes. To correct, use light eye shadow high and center.

EYE LINERS

They too are varied. Some very fine, others thicker, all formulated to slide onto the lid and hold, framing the eyes, shaping them, correcting faults, accenting color. Eye liner can match your eye shadow or your lashes, as you wish. It should be applied close to your lashes—but never on them! A well-directed stroke can make you someone new, someone exciting.

HOW TO APPLY EYE LINER

Whether you use the cake, pencil or liquid eye liner, the technique is the same. Look down into a magnifying mirror with the top tilted slightly toward you. Draw a fine line on the upper lid as close to the lashes as possible; extend it up and out slightly. Lift the upper lid slightly as you apply. It will help to give a smoother surface to the line. It takes a little practice, but you'll learn to make a precise hair line, curve it, and widen it for drama. The most dramatic effect is created with liquid eye liner, which goes on a little heavier and is less apt to run or smear. (But first pat a little on the back of your hand to be sure your brush isn't loaded. If you use too much, your art work may look messy and overdone.)

EYE LINER POINTERS

To accent the *entire eye,* draw the line as finely as you can and as close to the lashes as possible around the entire eye. Always work from the inside corner to the outer corner.

Almond eyes. Draw eye liner on the outer half of the upper lid and the outer half of the lower lid, lifting the lines deliberately at the outer corner.

Rounder eyes. Line only the outer half of the upper lid. Do *not* lift at the outer corner.

Sultry eyes. Line the upper lid a little more heavily from inner corner to outer corner.

MARVELS OF MASCARA

To me mascara has always had a very definite magic. This is a personal matter. All my life I've adored the theater and the illusion and charm a great actress can weave with words and gestures, but without the added magic of expressive eyes these words and gestures are meaningless. When I was very young only actresses dared to use mascara. "No wonder their eyes glow with such intensity," I thought. Not until many years later was I able to adopt this behind-the-footlight grandeur for everyday use and bring it to women everywhere.

Today what woman would be without mascara? And she doesn't have to carry it in a little box, wet it, and brush it on. Now it comes in graceful wands with spiraled tips that roll on the color, curl and separate the lashes all in one. Tiny particles have been added to some mascaras so that as you color, and repeat, these particles build up and extend the lashes themselves. Sweeping lashes can be rolled on in a few strokes. Best of all, you can get mascaras that are waterproof! No more worries about mascara-streaked cheeks. The colors are fixed so that they hold fast under the most trying circumstances.

THE RIGHT WAY AND THE WRONG WAY
TO PUT ON MASCARA

The right way. Whether you use cake mascara, an automatic applicator, liquid, or cream mascara, it should be stroked on in long even strokes from the roots of the lashes to the tips. A steady hand is required and no blinking or turning your head from side to side. Coat the lashes with two or three thin applications. After the first application, allow to dry a few seconds, then repeat. Lashes appear thick, natural, and longer.

The wrong way. Coating upper and lower lashes with one thick, sticky coat which glues them together and causes mascaraed clumps of lashes.

CONCERNING MASCARA COLORS

Mascaras come in basic colors which most women prefer for daytime use and special colors to create color illusion. The basics are black, brown, light brown, charcoal gray. Black is dramatic but rather stark for any but the true raven-haired brunette. Brown will seem very dark but is much softer. Light brown on a blonde often seems deep and dark enough. For the fair-skinned, fair-haired woman or one with silver hair there is charcoal gray. It's a delightful accent without harshness.

Midnight blue, by its very name, suggests that it is essentially for use when artificial light makes it seem blacker than black. Emerald green, royal blue, and violet are intended to accentuate eye color especially at night when overhead light threatens to rob them of clear color. Artifice always seems reasonable when we are frankly making an effort to be glamorous.

MASCARA MAGIC

By tipping just the center lashes on the upper lid, heavily, the eyes can be made to appear rounder.

Fringing the entire upper lashes with several mascara coats gives them extra length and sweep.

Mascara tipped on the outer half of the eyelashes, on the upper and lower lids, seems to make bulging eyes look less so.

Tip a few of the outer lashes on the upper eyelid and you achieve that slightly quizzical lift—youthful for an older face, pert for a younger.

A former editor of *Vogue* once told me in confidence, "I may go out hatless, sometimes forget my gloves, but without my mascara I feel naked!" And she was right, for time had thinned and lightened her lashes. Mascara, even a tiny bit, took ten years from her eyes.

THE BROW BEAUTIFUL

Each of us, I think, is curiously aware of some one aspect of total personality . . . an involuntary focus. I love eyebrows.

Eyebrows are interesting because they are unique, endlessly varied. Every pair of eyebrows has a natural distinction. They tend to follow the bony structure above the eye, acting as a protective cushion. A few hairs plucked here and there, a little color, and a brow that before seemed characterless can become lovely. *But proceed with caution.*

Flattering eyebrows

Hold a pencil straight up from nostril to brow. This is the natural starting point of your brow. Then slant the pencil from nostril to brow tip, crossing the outer corner of the eye—this is the terminal point. If the eyebrow is longer, pluck away the few straggling hairs with tweezers. (Always dip tweezers in alcohol before using them.) Then pluck any hairs on the bridge of the nose.

Some people insist the brow should arch at a point on the brow directly above the pupil of the eye. There is no rule about this. I believe it is better not to change the natural arch of the brow too radically. If the eyebrows tend to descend on the eyes and you want to raise the arch a fraction, pluck a few hairs judiciously from the lower edge of the brow. But go carefully—a few hairs can make an enormous difference.

Bear in mind eyes look larger in direct proportion to the manner in which the brow lifts. As one matures, the space between the brow and the eye tends to diminish—an almost imperceptible sag sets in. A few hairs discreetly removed along the lower edge of the brow helps to create that wide-eyed look of youth.

COLORING THE BROWS

Three aids to eyebrow coloring are:

1. the pencil—in a galaxy of shades and textures
2. brush-on powders in basic brow shades which cling to the brows, and
3. the bleaches.

Brow colors work up darker when used over color. This is why you must use color here sparingly and lightly. Otherwise even sparse brows can suddenly look heavy and overbearing.

PENCILING A BROW

When you wish to pencil a brow, feathery brief strokes like the hairs of the brow themselves are the most natural. Don't try too desperately to match your brow color. A shade slightly darker or lighter, blended in, is apt to look more as if it had grown there.

BRUSHING ON A BROW

The latest brow make-up gives a very soft effect as compared to the better-known eyebrow pencil. You brush on a clinging powder with a brush that is cut slantwise. Tip the point of the brush toward the inside of the eye, gradually turning the brush so you finish with the tip of the brush touching the tip of the brow. The effect is velvety —not quite as lasting as a pencil, but softer, and especially effective if you want to create brows that are fuller and more shapely.

BLEACHING A BROW

Hair coloring that changes the brunette to a blonde can sometimes leave her with brows so black they look incongruous. They can be bleached, *but never at home!* Your eyes are far too valuable to risk—this must be done only in a salon, by a careful operator. There you can close your eyes, lie back, and keep your eyes closed under protective pads until the job is done.

EYE CORRECTIVES

Deep-set eyes can have a coming-out party of their own. Band light pastel shadow or liner near the lashes, drawing or brushing it on to give more curve to the lids. Line a stronger color above the first crease in the upper eyelid. Blend toward outer corners. Fingertip blend ever so slightly up and out. Brows should be lifted by carefully plucking hairs at lower edge.

Round prominent eyes are put in their place by creating an elongation to offset the roundness. Shade on a medium gray or brown shadow just above the iris, out and up to the brow. Use a very thin eye liner near eye lashes and extend the brow line a trifle. Only a slight touch of light-shade mascara should be used.

Below the brow bulges are due to the bony structure being craggy or jutting out, but frequently they result from illness, age, and fatigue. You can cut down unwanted prominence by darkening the bulge with a gray or brown shadow to reduce reflected light. Now add the distraction of a lighter green, blue, or turquoise close to the lashes.

Small eyes call for the full battery of treatment.

Eye shadow, liner, and mascara. And if they still refuse to light up, artificial lashes. But first try shadow blended from lash to brow in a clean sweep up and out. Keep the darkest color area close to the lash line, and when you use eye liner, taper from thick to thin, starting from the inner eye corner.

Try on eye shadows, liners, mascaras, false eyelashes. Play with the various shades and colors. In the end you may decide merely to brush mascara on the outer tip of your upper lashes and glisten the upper lid with a colorless cream. But remember that you can change the entire expression of your face by the use of clever eye make-up. From being a nice unnoticed girl you can become a glamorous creature. Devote real time and effort to finding *the* eye make-up that is right for you —even if it means breaking all the rules and working out a new approach of your own.

ABOUT MOUTH MAKING

If the eyes and the eyebrows speak, the mouth, too, has its own story to tell of the personality. The small bee-stung mouth of the 1900s . . . the dainty bow of Clara Bow in the twenties . . . the wide, wonderful mouth of Joan Crawford, and now the natural, expressive mouth of Audrey Hepburn. The mouths of today are unconstrained, laughing, sensuous, and free.

The great pair of mouth makers are the lipstick and the lip brush. Many women are content with the lipstick alone, but the brush offers you added finesse. It outlines the shape more accurately, corrects it more precisely, and shades it with ease. Once you've accustomed yourself to the use of the lip brush, you'll never be without one. And the finest sable brush, meticulously pointed, lasts a long, long time. There is also a lipstick now that has a special way with curves and contours. Long and slim, to balance easily in the hand, it makes applying lipstick simpler than ever to do clearly and well.

Lip Shaping

Avoid pointed angular lines or straight sharp slashes of color. Draw wide, pleasant curves, following the natural lip line as nearly as possible.

Many make-up technicians feel lips should be closed

when lipstick is applied. Rest the little finger on the chin for better control, and with elbow on the dressing table:

1. Brush on lower lip (right over your dry, lightly powdered lips) by drawing a short horizontal line at lowest part of the lower lip.

2. Outline from left corner to center in rounded contour.

3. Outline from right corner to center, rounding the line.

4. Fill in with brush.

5. Draw two short vertical lines in center of upper lip, directly below the center of the nostrils. This represents the high point of the upper lip.

6. Outline from left corner to center.

7. Outline from center to right corner.

8. Fill in with brush.

A large mouth will look smaller simply by cutting the corners. Cover the natural lip line with a covering foundation. Set this more firmly by drying (lay a tissue over it to absorb moisture.) Set with a drop of skin freshener patted on with fingertips.

Keep the color line just inside the natural edge. Use subdued lipstick. Avoid very light, bright colors.

A small mouth may be built up by rounding the top curves right to the outer corners. Extend the line slightly below the natural edge on the bottom lip to balance both lips. Use light, bright colors.

A droopy mouth may be given a provocative upward tilt by lifting the lining stroke ever so slightly at the outer corners of the upper lip.

For lips that look soft, blot the first lipstick application with a tissue. For extra gloss apply a second coat but don't blot.

For lips that last, use the above technique, but powder the lips between applications.

Two Shades of Lipstick May Be Better Than One

Light colors enlarge; dark or subdued colors minimize. Use a light color, just one shade removed from the darker, on whichever lip you want to bring forward. In this way you can equalize a pouty underlip with a more constrained upper lip, or enlarge a thin underlip with lighter color.

227

Lipstick color should harmonize with your skin color and your hair. Your lipstick collection can be started with one light and one deeper tone lipstick particularly flattering to the skin and the colors you are currently wearing. Then for corrective modeling you can add as many new fashion shades as you wish each season. If you wear blues and violets you will want at least one shade with a blue note; one also in the golden family, to bring out the best in your browns, beiges, yellows, and greens, and a clear true red to flash against black and white. Some of the neutral shades look soft and lovely outdoors.

Generally speaking, brunettes wear intense, bright shades, blondes, redheads, and the gray-haired find soft, light-to-medium shades more becoming. Younger girls obtain soft, flattering effects with the paler lipstick colors, and mature women find that lighter shades of the colors they wore earlier are most charming for them.

In my New York salon we devised and time-tested a fifteen-minute make-up routine to last all day.

On skin that has been thoroughly cleansed and refreshed with lotion, apply a protective layer of moisturizing cream. Blot off excess with tissues. (Time: 1 minute.)

Put a few drops of foundation in palm of hand. With fingertips of other hand, place five dots on face—forehead, nose, cheeks, chin. Blend with entire hand (not just fingertips), using firm up-and-out strokes. Blot excess with tissues. (Time: 1 minute.)

Mix liquid rouge with a little foundation in palm of hand. Place three dots on each cheekbone. Blend with fingertips till there is no indication where nature leaves off and art takes over. (Time: 2 minutes.)

Press on powder firmly in this order: forehead, eyebrows, eyelids, entire nose, cheeks, lower part of face, lips, chin, under chin. To avoid the necessity of making up the neck and perhaps marking your clothes, choose foundation and powder that matches the skin tone of your neck. (Time: ½ minute.)

Remove excess powder from around eyes with clean puff; brush it off eyebrows. Apply eye shadow generously near lash line, then blend up and out. Shadow applied freely can be blended more easily and the excess is easily blotted away. Shadow applied too sparingly will streak. (Time: 1 minute.)

✓ Carefully apply waterproof liquid eye liner with sable brush close to lash line, on upper lids only. (Time: 4 minutes.)

✓ Apply mascara to upper lashes only. (Time: 1 minute.)

✓ With a piece of fresh cotton, gently dust off all excess powder, using downward movements. (Time: ½ minute.)

✓ Using eyebrow pencil, feather in the brows to form a gentle arch. Darken only as much as hair and skin tones will allow. (Time: 2 minutes.)

✓ Shape and color lips. (Time: 2 minutes.)

If you are a beginner, the first time you follow this routine it may take a little longer than fifteen minutes. But with practice it will take less time.

If you have one more minute to spare, there's an extra trick that's effective in hot weather, or when you're going to be out of doors all day, or if you have an oily-skin problem. You can "set" your make-up by going over face and neck with a pad of clean cotton, moistened in cold water with a few drops of astringent added. Pat on firmly but lightly. This gives your face an extra glow and a dewy look too.

Final advice to the older woman. Where make-up is concerned, your golden rule should be "a *little* of everything." Use it sparingly to give a natural look and to avoid an unbecoming "painted on" effect. Use your foundation, rouge, powder, lipstick color, brow pencil, mascara, lightly. Choose softly becoming shades; avoid heavy colors and a heavy hand.

Eye liners or shadows that settle in the tiny creases of the eyelids are aging. If you are blue-eyed use *light* blues and mauve shadows; if eyes are dark choose *light* turquoises, *pale* greens. Use lip colors in soft pinks or corals. Try dark brown or gray mascara, never black.

Eyebrows often present a problem to the mature woman. They may tend to "flop" as age settles the facial contours. You should pluck away most of the hairs under the brows and lightly pencil across the top lines of the brows. Brown and gray pencils—used lightly—one over the other, will give the most natural effect.

Rouge should go high on cheekbones and be smoothed out to a faint shading toward the temples. Cream rouge is, I believe, the easiest and most effective for you, always applied *over foundation*. Never let it stray below the nostril line as it draws too much attention to mouth lines and to the lower part of the face where early signs of aging may show first.

And now, whether you are sixteen or over sixty, remember, understatement is the rule of a fine make-up artist. Adjust your make-up to the light in which you wear it. Daylight reveals color; artificial light drains it.

Never be afraid to experiment. It is only by trying new colors and new techniques that you will be able to discover those things that will give you a new—and personally exciting—look of beauty.

7 } How to Manage Your Hair — and Glorify It

HAIR should be and can be every woman's crowning glory! Hair that is easy to handle can be coaxed into taking and holding just about any shape in the world that is becoming. Yet in this day and age, even the finest, most difficult hair can be prettily set and held in place with the help of specialized preparations that actually add body and give life to limp, stringy hair.

Anyone who says today that she "can't do a thing with her hair" is behind the times as far as all the fabulous new hair-care preparations are concerned.

And yet the hairbrush is still the most important means of assuring proper hair care. Although customs and tradition often change with time, nothing better has ever been found to assure a bright, shining, healthy head of hair than the proverbial 100 strokes of the hairbrush morning and night. Generally I am skeptical when I hear people say, "The best things in life are free." But I believe it when I see a lovely head of hair that has obviously been brushed and cared for since early youth—and proudly proclaims it!

When I was a girl I was most dissatisfied with my own

hair. It was so straight, so black, and none of the current fashions seemed flattering. You can be sure I tried everything, until I was forced to adopt the only style that seemed to suit me—brushing my hair straight back into a chignon at the nape of the neck. But the choice was a fortunate one at that, for with daily brushing my hair has retained its sparkle and still reaches to my waist.

Brushing stimulates the scalp and forces the natural oil of the hair to do a self-polishing and conditioning job. Your brush carries the oils to the hair ends which are always dry. When you brush from the scalp out, with your head down, pulling slightly as you flip the brush outward, every stroke rouses the circulation and encourages the flow of blood to the scalp, which in turn nourishes the hair follicles.

You will notice, when starting such a routine, that your hair appears greasier. Gradually it shows more vigor, sheen increases, it falls into place more easily when you set it. The young look seems to stage a comeback, and, as the weeks pass, the oiliest hair tends to normalize, dry hair looks better, and dandruff-ridden hair is cleared of its flakiness.

In view of the importance of brushing, I encourage our salon clientele to indulge in the finest brushes with natural bristles. Tapered, natural bristles penetrate the hair more smoothly, have a pickup that helps to spread the oils, and are less apt to break the hair. Besides, a good brush has a long life if properly cared for.

Cleanliness is essential in brushing. The cleaner your brush, the better your hair behaves. A dirty brush—if you happen to have infectious dandruff—tends to reinfect the scalp. I have found that placing a large terry towel across the knees and wiping the brush on it frequently during brushing sessions rids the brush of the dust and light surface dirt.

A little understanding of the hair itself may be helpful. Hair is nourished by the blood stream. It is the most important offshoot of the skin. Each fully grown hair consists of a tapering shaft ending in a bulb which is enclosed in a follicle. The average life of a scalp hair appears to vary from a few months to six years, with a normal range of two to four years.

When a hair is about to be shed, a void or empty space is formed between the bulb of the hair and the center portion of the hair shaft. Gradually the hair shaft is loosened and falls out, leaving an empty hair follicle, and a new hair grows in.

Remember that your hair is a mirror of your general health! Drastic diets may dry it out . . . you can starve it as you starve yourself. Nervous tension affects it. The sun can dry it out, too, and excessive teasing can produce considerable thinning.

I've often heard women say, "But I'm eating a well-balanced diet." They don't seem to recognize that occasionally the body fails to absorb the nutrients it is offered. You could be eating well and your hair could be starving to death! Glandular imbalance, so often a problem of middle age, can be a contributing cause. Your doctor will know how to adjust this. Hereditary factors also seem to play a role in thinning hair at middle age. You can camouflage thinning hair by using hair styles with no visible part lines or filling in bare places with a partial hair piece.

Hair lacking in body. Brush it, stimulate it, promote circulation! Let the faster blood flow contribute to your hair. Steal a few extra hours of sleep each night. Try a new protein conditioner. Add a cream rinse to give a "lift" to your locks. Hair coloring seems to help, as some hair coloring products condition and add body as they color.

Fine hair will always be fine, but it is also silky soft and when lively has a satin sheen. A good blunt cut will make it appear more bulky. Such hair appears thicker and easier to set and arrange when it has had a body permanent especially created for fine hair.

Coarse hair is usually healthy, bouncy, heavy, and durable. A special cut by a good hair stylist will help keep it in shape. But the hairbrush is still your outstanding friend as it will distribute the natural oils and keep your hair shining and disciplined.

Curly hair is a nuisance when there are many straight-haired fashions, but now many new Paris fashions are short and curly. Jumbo rollers and conditioners to prevent dryness will take away some of the super-curliness.

A smart stylist can cut naturally curly hair so that it lies in a more controlled way . . . or take advantage of the curl to give hair a more lasting set.

Straight hair is seldom totally straight. It usually has some hint of a curl. Often when it is cut shorter, tapered, or layered, a natural wave will appear if one is desired. Straight hair is most beautiful when brushed to a high gloss and set in a simple style. Its drama depends on sheen and color. Both are easy to acquire.

Dry, brittle hair needs a cream dressing and a special cream rinse treatment following every shampoo. Daily massage will bring the blood coursing to the scalp. Brushing will give the hair polish and will make it more manageable.

Excessively oily hair can be controlled by washing two or three times a week with a shampoo made specially for this condition. Sometimes a soft permanent makes this hair more porous, so it can absorb some of the excess oil. Fingertip massage is as important for oily hair as for dry hair. Even though at first you feel the brushing and massage make the hair seem oilier, in time they help it to become self-regulating.

Dandruff is not so much dangerous as annoying and unsightly. Some dead cell drift is normal, but when it speeds up, it's not. There are many explanations given and as many attempts to solve this problem. Some specialists feel dandruff is due to the malfunction of the sebaceous glands; others think it's due to faulty metabolism, poor circulation, inadequate diet, the wrong kind of cleansing, or hormone imbalance and even nerves—all have been termed at different times the cause of dandruff.

I would put absolute cleansing and frequent shampooing with plenty of brushing before and after as "musts" on my list. Certain dandruff-remover shampoos are also helpful. This is especially true if you just happen to have simple dandruff. But if you have inflammation and redness at the scalp, you should see your doctor. (Don't try to treat this condition yourself.) Dandruff is not dangerous. Dandruff is simply something you must try to correct since it can also affect the condition of your skin.

Hair Styles

Many women come to my salons and ask, with a wistful expression, "How do I know which hair style I can wear? There are so many to choose from, and I'm afraid I might pick the wrong one!"

Of course, the ideal is to find a hair stylist with golden scissors and impeccable taste. He takes over your hair without a single directive, and creates the perfect style for you. Unfortunately such master hair stylists are usually booked solid for months ahead, or their charges won't fit your budget, or you live in a small town where expert hair stylists are not available. Then what?

Remember your hats? Remember their shapes, sizes, and forms—the most becoming ones—and act accordingly. Have you always found a pillbox placed squarely on top of your head flattering? You'll find a hair style close to your head with a fluffy pillbox of curls where your hat would have been, or a chignon about the same size to pin on in the same spot, equally flattering.

Are you a person who likes turbans—turbans that sit back on the head, close around the face, and with a good deal of drapery placed at the crown? For you, there is a hair style that loosely hugs your face, picks up on the crown toward the back of your head. Or a short cut, sleek at the sides with some upsweep or chignon interest where turban fullness might have been.

Think of your hair as the hat nature has given you and see what can be done with it. This is a particularly valid theory when so many women are appearing bareheaded at even the most formal functions, and on city streets well-dressed women wear nothing on their heads but a wisp of veiling or a bow pinned on short hair. Tints, rinses, and sprays that turn hair into lasting confections of form and color have helped to bring about this swing in fashion.

Personally, I have always loved hats, and being somewhat old-fashioned, I wouldn't dream of appearing hatless in a sophisticated city before nightfall. It's a question of individual taste. Most young women, particularly if they have lovely hair, look well hatless, but for the right function a cleverly chosen hat adds to your poise and your elegance.

THE FASHIONABLE HEAD

Each season sees a new type of hair style that we read about in magazines and hear about among our friends as being "fashionable." Literally this means a hair fashion that has been designed by stylists thinking in terms of the latest lines in dresses from Paris and the newest millinery. Sometimes they look a little strange to us because the eye has not accustomed itself to this change of pace. Sooner or later, however, last year's hair fashions become very understandable, no longer shocking, and only a startlingly "different" one stops anybody for a second. Just being different and extreme in fashions is not necessarily being fashionable. Everything depends on the mood and the line.

My advice would be—look at the news in hair fashions, but adopt only the style which is becoming to you personally. Then you cannot go wrong. Remember, too, the best hair fashions are invariably the simplest.

Never try to cut your own hair. This is one job you really must leave to an expert, that is, if you are going to have a chic, easily managed coiffure. The expenditure will more than pay for itself in satisfaction and will permit your coiffure to reflect the three faces of fashion.

1. *Face toward the Country*

The casual style that can go to the country and be wind-blown and wind-tossed, yet come up with a definite form and a becoming shape.

2. *Face toward Town*

The same cut adapted for a smoother "town" look, emphasizing the fashionable feeling of the moment.

3. *Face toward Formal Events*

The third face of fashion turns toward evening, and this same hair style, with minor changes, shows a dramatic difference when worn with current evening fashions.

If you have never thought of your hair as having three faces toward fashion, begin now to think this way. You will be surprised how much more attractive you and your clothes will seem. When the hair style is suitable the clothes seem more suitable too.

Hair Color

The easy application of hair color is one of the greatest innovations of this decade. Just because you were born a mousy blonde is no reason why you have to remain forever unhappy about it. You now have the freedom to choose your own hair color as if it were a cosmetic.

However, experimenting with hair color should be done carefully. The wonderful thing about hair color is that it comes in so many different variations. If a woman is uncertain about the color she wants for herself she can gradually work her way from a semipermanent rinse to a permanent tint. I always recommend getting expert advice before taking the final plunge.

Semipermanent rinses last through several shampoos—five or more, in fact. They don't lighten dark hair, but they do blend in grays. They can turn white and light gray hair blond, tan-with-gold, russet, brown or black. They can bring out golden lights in blonde hair and even unearth a copper glow that is especially lovely against a sun-tanned skin. There are dozens of shades, including many silver ones. You may long to be free of yellowing threads among the silver—or you might prefer silver instead of snow-white hair.

At one time I was considered a conservative about the use of hair color. I still am, particularly where the very young are concerned. I don't approve of teen-agers indiscriminately changing the color of their hair "just for kicks." But, having experimented with the newest hair coloring aids for the past few years, I can assure you that these products are wonderfully safe when used as directed. If intelligently used, they can certainly make many women look younger and more glamorous. I don't advocate a radical change in hair coloring unless it is first supervised by an expert. If your dullish brown hair displeases you, by all means become a blonde—but do so with care, with professional help, otherwise you may be very disappointed with the results. Then, with experience, you can afford to be more daring. There are wonderful permanent tints easy enough to handle at home. But you must dedicate a small amount of time every three or four weeks to carefully maintaining the color you have decided on.

COLOR SELECTION

Don't be too drastic. A change of twenty shades at one sitting is a drastic procedure. Besides it can be very hard on the hair. Going from brunette to blond, one must reduce pigmentation sharply, whereas the change from carrot-red to deep, lustrous red-brown is a simple color reach and may be enormously becoming.

One of the safest rules to follow is to choose a hair color in the same color family as your own hair. A blonde might go from pale blond to smoky ash blond, or from ash blond to golden blond, and the chances are the color would be extremely attractive with her skin tone. (Of course you can modify your skin tone with make-up.)

Generally speaking, the woman past forty will find a lighter shade of her own natural youthful hair coloring more flattering than trying to repeat the exact color she remembers as being hers earlier. For example, raven hair can be tinted a glossy deep brown with lighter brown or gold highlights, or even a deep ash blond, and it will be softer and prettier than black hair framing a skin that is no longer young.

You must remember that color can be changed in one of two ways. The natural pigment of the hair can be bleached and lightened, or artificial coloring can be applied to the hair. Frequently it will be necessary to do both to obtain the desired effect. Although there are many types of hair coloring preparations, the major products are bleaches, temporary color rinses, semipermanent and permanent hair coloring preparations.

Bleaches

Bleaches are used to lighten the hair by removing some

of the natural pigmentation. If it is desired to lighten the hair by more than two shades, *pre-bleaching* is required. In pre-bleaching, the bleach is mixed with a hair lightener and applied to bleach out much or all of the color. This is done to gain extreme lightening prior to blond toning. A *toner*, which is a highly diluted tint, is usually applied after pre-bleaching.

Temporary color rinses

These bring out natural highlights and last until washed away with the next shampoo. Sometimes they are sold in capsule form, but highlighting shampoos are also available.

Semi-permanent hair coloring preparations (sometimes called color rinses)

Some of these have been developed to such a degree that they last through as many as five shampoos. They brighten and intensify natural color and offer a certain amount of coverage when hair is beginning to gray, by blending the lighter hair into the darker, giving a more even-toned color.

Permanent hair color preparations (tints)

Tints are usually in shampoo form and must be used with an oxidizing agent such as hydrogen peroxide to develop hair color. A tint penetrates the hair shaft into the center layer of the hair to produce a permanent effect. Tints may lighten the hair, but unless the hair is pre-bleached the degree of lightening is limited to no more than two shades. Many tints now contain conditioning elements for a more lustrous look. (Tints are also known as hair dyes.)

When you decide on your first coloring, it is a good thing to let a professional do it. You can learn so much while you're seeing someone else do the job, and even if you repeat it yourself hundreds of times thereafter, you will learn from this first application.

Above all, read directions and follow them exactly. When you are dealing with hair coloring, you are dealing with chemical changes. You cannot wipe it on and wipe it off like lipstick. Do not try to improvise, make no experiments . . . do *not* try to be original! I know that women, being highly creative, often tend to innovate. This is a marvelous thing, and in every other aspect of cosmetics and make-up it is a quality I approve of and admire. But hair coloring is too complex for an amateur to fool with.

Color and change your hair; discover a beauty you may never have known; but do it carefully, and do it according to directions followed to the letter.

The Wonder of Wigs

I know of a lady commentator on TV who must rush from one television studio to another and yet always look her best for the cameras. Her solution is to own several wigs—casual, formal, long and short styles, with one or another usually at the hairdresser's to be coiffed. The average woman's life scarcely calls for anything so elaborate, but this lady is known as one of the best-dressed women on the air—she never has a hair out of place.

Lest you get the impression wigs are radical, I am reminded of a young banker's wife who attends conventions with her husband and takes along a duplicate of her own short Italian hair style, carefully coiffed. She finds that the annoyance of having her fine hair set when she should be active with her husband and his friends has now become no problem at all. Who bought her this wig? Her sensible husband, who recognized that the cost was nothing compared to his wife's peace of mind and the charming effect she creates.

Remember that wigs are not necessarily full hair pieces. They can be clusters of curls, chignons, a braid, a piece designed to fit among your top front hair, or a body-building bang—or an extension of your hair that fits in on the crown to give you back-head fullness where you need it most.

Today wigs have become so attractive women no longer bother to hide the fact that they wear them. Some take pride in owning several. I like wigs. I feel they are right for this fast-moving age in which many women do two or even three jobs. They save time, and in a hard-pressed life where the unexpected is always happening, they are one more answer to that old cry, "Whatever can I do about my hair?"

8 } Hands, Fingers, and Nails
. . . Toes and Toenails

HANDS can reveal character and express emotions. They can also convey the essence of beauty with every gesture. Moving or in repose, they tell their own story of inner composure, uncertainty, excitement, even love. Hands clutching at themselves, picking threads, lighting cigarettes, busy without apparent purpose—all tell of strain or of inner tension. Then there are the calm, composed hands. They move like birds with grace and rhythm, informing even the casual stranger of a serene, orderly mind. Beautiful hands can do more to give an "impression" of beauty than most people realize.

How would a stranger assess your hands? Can you place them in your lap as gracefully as a lady in a portrait, and keep them there quietly? The first thing to learn about beautiful hands is that they must be beautiful in repose.

Try this simplest of hand exercises. Seat yourself in a straight chair. Push the small of your back against it. Sit tall, holding your head up from the back of the neck. Your stomach is in, your bosom high. Now sit quietly for a full two minutes. Breathe in—pause. Breathe out—pause. Practice this several times in private, keeping your mind serene. It is important to hold the position without effort. Your feet are on the floor, the heel of one touching the instep of the other. Your chin is lifted. Your hands are in your lap slightly opened, one resting across the other, with the palms up. Or you may reverse them, with palms down. You've seen this pose in paintings of a Chinese empress, an English court lady, a Spanish aristocrat. To sit at ease and manage your hands is one of the most elementary lessons in achieving dignity and poise. It marks you as a person of ease and grace.

Now stand in front of a mirror and see how gracefully you can use your hands as you pretend to tell a story. Keep the gestures small, in a limited area. Let your hands talk, but with discretion—they should not say a word too many. Gestures should be meaningfully controlled.

Protect Your Hands. Whenever you use your hands for home tasks such as washing dishes or linens, keeping them for any length of time in soapy water, be sure they carry a protective coating of hand lotion for the job. Some of the lotion will wash away—but the skin of your hands will be less exposed to harsh detergents than if they had gone to the task bare. Nowadays it is no longer necessary to use extremely hot water, strong soaps or harsh detergents. One of the blessings of modern living is a cold water soap, usually found in powder form. All that is required is to briefly soak your delicate underthings or woolen sweaters in cold water with a few spoonfuls of this special soap. Swish them around several times, rinse in clear cold water, and there you are. The work is done and your hands are as soft as ever. (Small individual packets of this cold water soap are a boon to the traveler.) Wearing rubber gloves can also be helpful but before putting them on it is wise to lubricate the hands with a softening hand lotion.

For Garden Lovers. There are cotton gloves to protect the hands, but if you feel the need to have direct contact with the earth (and the best gardeners always do), work in some white soap under your nails *before* you begin. And be sure to apply your favorite hand cream before you get down to the more arduous task of transplanting. An important rule for gardeners is to keep the nails trim and short.

How to Protect Aging Hands. This is a problem I face daily, and at night, before going to bed, I cleanse and massage my hands with the same care that I lavish on my face—working the cream in with squeezing, circling, pinching motions from base to fingertip, manipulating each finger separately. I leave the cream on overnight as a protective coating to keep my hands soft. It also helps to lighten freckles and check "age spots." Yes, I go to bed wearing an old pair of white cotton gloves to keep the cream where it belongs; instead of on the bed linen.

Here are a few extra "tips" for aging hands.

When there is no enamel on your nails, apply wrappings of cotton dipped in warm mineral oil over each fingertip. They can be worn at night under your protective cotton gloves, or any time of the day when you have a few free moments. This is marvelous for the nails, and any overflow of oil will only aid the hands.

Try a mask treatment occasionally at the knuckles and back up to the wrist.

MANICURES

Whenever I've written a book on beauty (and throughout the years there have been several), someone has remarked, "Aren't you going to include manicure instructions?" Surely everyone by now must know the basic rules of manicure—but sometimes people forget such important details as *not* filing down into the corners. This can cause trouble.

So for the beauty beginner, and for those who might like to check their present methods against my classic salon manicure, here are the basic steps.

1. Remove the old polish thoroughly with an oily polish remover. Moisten cotton and press it against the nail for several seconds. Do not rub back and forth or round and round. Repeat if necessary.

2. Rinse off remover with lukewarm water.

3. With an orangewood stick tipped with cotton and moistened with cuticle remover, push back the cuticle gently, working around the base and sides and under the nail tips. (Never cut the cuticle. Snip off hangnails with nipper when necessary.)

4. Wash hands again and rub off any dead cuticle.

5. With an emery board (not a metal file), shape the nails into neat ovals, being careful not to file the nails deep down at the corners as this can cause splitting. Smooth the edges with the fine side of an emery board.

6. With hands steadied on table top, apply a coat of polish base coat. Allow to dry.

7. Apply polish. Using two coats insures much longer wear and a deeper intensity of color. Make the first coat thin and the second coat slightly heavier. Remove a hairline of polish from nail tips with ball of thumb of opposite hand.

8. Apply nail polish sealer while nails are still slightly damp.

9. Always repair chipped polish immediately.

10. Use pink, coral, or red shades of polish (exceptions to this are the use of iridescents, gold and silver for evening).

11. Extra benefit: occasionally "rest" nails without polish and buff with short, quick strokes to give them a lovely natural gloss.

12. If you are troubled with nails that split, peel, break, or chip, don't hesitate to use a special nail hardener *after* you have given yourself a manicure but *before* polishing. This should be done twice a week, for the first two weeks, in a double application. Thereafter, once a week is sufficient until you are completely satisfied with the condition of your nails.

Beautiful Feet

Once in Rome I occupied an apartment on the Via Veneto which had a charming terrace not too far above the street. I sometimes had my meals on this terrace as I enjoyed watching the people strolling by on a summer evening or hurrying to work in the morning. How revealing it was! As I looked down, I could see well-dressed women walking as if their feet hurt. They did not distribute their weight correctly. They looked old and sloppy. And then a working woman would stroll by, regal, poised.

She knew how to walk! It was then I became aware of feet—the neglected allies of beauty.

No woman whose feet ache can look beautiful. She picks her way as if on hot coals. Her tired feet shuffle in an effort to spare one, then the other, foot. She doesn't sit because she wants to but because she can't stand for another moment the weight pressing on her arches. And this is a hurt that increases with each pound above the normal weight for age and height. In fact, women often find that, freed of twenty or thirty extra pounds of excess weight to carry, their feet suddenly feel young and light again.

Actually the feet that fetch and carry for you seldom get their share of beauty attention. I suspect this is because calluses and corns are not apparent under hose and shoes. But the increasing fashion for bare legs and for shoes with toes and heels exposed has begun to awaken women to the need of caring for their feet. Beautiful feet, throughout the ages, have always been considered one of the most seductive assets a woman can possess.

Here is my basic program for foot health and beauty.

A daily bath or foot soak. This is just as important as regular cleansing of the face and hands. Perhaps you haven't time for a full bath, but you can always fill the tub partially, throw a towel over the edge, and perch for five minutes . . . while you wiggle your toes in warm water, bring the water up to hot, and then finish with cold. This simple bathing at the end of a tiring day leaves those numb, worn-out feet feeling more like wings, less like weights.

Table salt or Epsom salts used in foot baths will refresh even further. Remember the joys of wading in the ocean? A salt foot bath feels just as cool and refreshing in the tub, and the Epsom treatment draws tiredness out of aching feet.

Keep your feet dry. Following your foot bath, be sure to dry your feet thoroughly, especially between the toes. This discourages the development of athlete's foot and other common foot fungus infections. After a bath or swim, pat your feet dry with a soft towel and then let them air for a few minutes. It is also wise to dust them liberally with a good foot powder, especially between the toes where perspiration can be annoying and damaging. Sprinkle powder on your feet morning and night, after the bath, before slipping into your stockings, and shake a little powder into your shoes whenever you change your footwear. This is added insurance against accumulating moisture. And since nylon hose does not absorb perspiration, these protective hints are essential.

✔ *Keep an eye out for minor foot blemishes*—and treat them promptly. Some of the special foot aids for corns, calluses, and blisters deserve a spot on a well-stocked beauty shelf. You can find them in almost any drug or dime store. They can relieve pressure from shoes and prevent big or little foot irritations.

✔ Learn to give yourself a professional pedicure. This is almost identical with your manicure except for a few minor details. It does require proper supplies—a toenail file, toenail nippers (not those designed for fingernails), an orangewood stick, cuticle oil, and of course the same colored nail polish that you use on your fingertips. Dip the orangewood stick in oil and gently push back the cuticles. Then clean carefully under and around the toenails. When you trim them, always cut straight across. This is the important difference between doing the toenails and the fingernails. By curving the toenails you could very easily encourage ingrown toenails. If you cannot manage to give yourself a pedicure, visit a professional once a month. I am a great believer in regular visits to a good pedicurist.

✔ *Choose your footwear with care.* This means getting a perfect fit in hosiery, bedroom slippers, tennis shoes, as well as your everyday pumps and flats. Poorly fitted footwear can cause "pump bumps," misshapen toes, poor posture, and the whole gamut of corns, calluses, and blisters. There should be ample room across the toes, a firm arch support, and a heel height appropriate to the amount of walking you do.

✔ *Massage and exercise.* Feet need a workout too, to remain in top condition. One simple exercise to strengthen the foot muscles is to pick up marbles or other small objects with your toes. Foot massage helps keep up the circulation and prevent swollen feet and ankles. Use a foot balm to massage your feet after your bath; gently manipulate and pull each toe and rub the tops and soles of the feet vigorously.

For weak or aching arches and toes, try these simple exercises.

To limber toes. Sit in a chair and rest first your right foot and then the left on a telephone book so that toes stretch over the unbound edge. Then riffle the pages with your toes.

To stretch calf muscles (when high heels get you down). Stand barefoot about two feet from the wall. Turn toes in with weight on outer edges of the feet. With palms against the wall and arms bent, try to touch the wall with your head, keeping head up, back straight, heels on floor.

To strengthen arches. Stand with feet parallel and roll both feet outward at the same time.

Dead-tired feet. Seated on the edge of the bed, place both hands behind your knees and hold this position firmly. Now relax your ankles as you would your wrists, and shake firmly, first one ankle, then the other. At first you may find it hard to relax the feet, but keep trying. This simple exercise is amazingly refreshing. You will soon be able to shake your toes with almost the same freedom as your fingers when you do finger-relaxing exercises.

Sore metatarsal arch. Feet ache? Perhaps you walked too far on high heels. After your foot bath rub a little of your richest emollient cream on your feet, and tug each toe as you rub, especially the big toe. Now grasp the foot firmly across the base of the toes, on the under side of the foot, and press your fingers hard and up from the thick cushiony place behind the toes in the area between the big and little toes. Work up toward the inner arch. Keep repeating this motion from the metatarsal arch to the instep, squeezing and pressing as you rub the cream in.

More toe limbering. Press one foot on the floor, stretching the toes apart as wide as you can, like stretching your fingers open. At first they'll stay closed. You must "think" them open till you can open and close your toes like the fingers on your hand. If the toes refuse to move, cuddle them gently while separating the toes with your fingers. Encourage this opening by pressing the forepart of the foot hard on the floor and "think" your little toe away from the foot. This toe limbering exercise helps to keep toes straightened out, and in time it will limber them up enormously.

TV toe exercise. Everyone in this day and age spends some time watching TV. Why not take advantage of this time to do some basic foot exercises? This is a good time to bring exhausted feet back into better shape. One of the simplest exercises (and it requires the least concentration) is to roll a bottle under the bare foot. Place the bottle under the metatarsal arch, force and roll forward to the toes. Now roll it back to the arch and press down firmly. Repeat this ten times, one foot at a time.

TAKE YOUR FEET OUT OF HIDING

Your feet live indoors far too much. I am speaking of those leather houses we lace around them and from which they so seldom emerge. No wonder many feet develop curious ailments, chilblains, calluses, corns, and bunions. They never have a chance to escape from their cramped prison quarters. Take off your shoes and let your feet feel free again. Walk around your house barefoot, or at least around your bedroom, and if you must put on shoes while you're at home, be sure they're open and airy—a sandal with a single thong, or perhaps Japanese grass slippers or loose scuffs.

Tiptoeing as you go about your household tasks is marvelous for exercising toes and arches. While you're barefoot, slip in one of the easiest exercises. Ankle pivots, for instance—the slow rotation of the foot at the ankle will literally fine down the ankle and get rid of any tiny gathering of fatty tissue in this area.

Do your feet seem large to you? Study the rest of your body. Nature is usually a fine sculptor with an excellent sense of proportion, giving you hands and feet that are well planned to carry your height and weight. If you are complaining about the size of your ankles or your feet, take a good look at your hands. You will begin to see that the feet Nature gave you are probably related to the size of your hands.

ANKLES

A large woman with a too fine ankle is like a huge piece of sculpture perched upon a pin. Many people with strong bone structure throughout their bodies need substantial underpinnings. By learning to place your feet properly when you stand, and walking with a good free stride from the hips, your ankles will develop strength while keeping their graceful line.

Among my business acquaintances was a New York store buyer who did much walking. She was proud of her small feet, but unhappy about her fatty-looking legs and ankles. Besides, her feet often ached and swelled so that they felt cramped inside her shoes, she told me. She was unable to get around as much as her work required, and it worried her. After a period of doing leg exercises and ankle pivots, which released the tension in her legs and feet while it slimmed them, I was able to convince her—it wasn't easy—that she needed a longer shoe size. It gave greater contrast to her ankles and created an illusion of slenderness.

Tuck this thought away in your memory. Shoes that are too small only succeed in making legs and ankles look heavier.

9 ⟩ Fresh ... Fragrant ...
and Ready for Anything

W<small>HEN</small> Madame de Montespan was the king's favorite at the French court of Louis XIV the pace in her small circle was as hectic as ours, yet she repeatedly journeyed from Paris to Provence by coach to take the "waters." These "waters" were the famous thermal baths discovered by the Romans who relished the health-giving, therapeutic effects of the volcanic water rising from deep rocky crevices—the same thermal baths known later throughout Europe as spas.

Today you have only to journey from your bedroom to your bath to enjoy baths that in their own way can be as relaxing and beauty building as any in which the Romans or Madame de Montespan luxuriated.

Bathrooms have never been more glamorous. A few years ago they were either functional or "girlish"—stark white or pink. Suddenly, the décor was changed. Bottles of bath oil, flacons of bath salts, colored soaps, towels and accessories add to the fantasy. The current fashion is for big, bold patterns in smashing contemporary colors. Towels and facecloths, shower curtains and bath mats are ebulliently colorful.

253

The color schemes of contemporary bathrooms are as exciting as the preparations that fill them—olive green, turquoise, and deep rich blue . . . watermelon pink, tangerine, lemon yellow. They invite a sense of happiness while you bathe and refurbish yourself.

THE BATH FOR RELAXATION

At the end of the day, draw a hot bath and empty a handful of bubble bath under the faucet till it foams. Nothing is more agreeably luxurious than an air-filled adjustable pillow for your tub. It clings in place with suction cups. You should also have a loose bathing cap to keep your hair in place and protected from steam.

After cleansing your face and running through your basic skin care routine, step into the tub, bringing with you your eye pads moistened with a refreshing herbal extrait. Settle back against the cushion, eye pads sealing out the view, and lie in the relaxing, perfumed water for ten minutes. The water should not be cold enough to rouse you or hot enough to debilitate. It's a wonderfully effective way to help soothe frazzled nerves and induce sleep.

THE TUB FACIAL

Steam and cream are good companions. When there's no time to give yourself a facial, take advantage of the steamy air from your hot bath to make your skin even more receptive to creams and to help combat skin dryness. After a thorough cleansing and toning, use your richest lubricating cream *after* you've stepped into the bath. The heat and humidity urge the skin to a fuller appreciation of oils and emollients. And after bathing, when you tissue off the remainder, you will be amazed to see how silky your skin has become.

THE REFRESHER BATH

People in tropical climates are surprised when they learn of our custom of taking cold baths to cool off in hot weather. It is the moderately warm bath, they insist, which is the most cooling. The cold bath is effective only until you've stepped out of it; whereas a warm bath in midsummer will induce perspiration for a few moments and leave you feeling comfortable and cool for hours afterward. (A cup of hot tea will have the same effect.)

Add a few drops of your favorite fragrance or bath oil to the bath. And don't dry too enthusiastically. You'll feel much cooler if you leave your skin just a trifle moist.

The moderately warm bath can be taken as often as you like in hot weather.

THE FRICTION BATH

I like nothing better than getting into a warm bath to which drops of fragrant bath oil have been added. For greater stimulus you might prefer a cool tub, gradually turning on the hot water while you rub your body all over with a good firm loofah bath mitt. This is a fibrous, loosely intertwined sponge that helps to increase your circulation and to scrub your skin really clean.

Once your body has been scrubbed down, soap thoroughly. Soak for a few minutes, then enjoy a cool rinse or shower.

The friction bath is primarily stimulating. It will wake you up and put you in an excellent mood.

THE SHOWER

Many Americans have become shower addicts, almost forgetting the delights of tub bathing. Showers are particularly good in the morning, as a stimulant, and wonderful coupled with a brisk body rub with a body lotion and a powder dusting. However, this exposure to water is no substitute for the long, relaxing soak. Of course much of it is a matter of habit. I am sure that to the Japanese our ten minutes in and out of the tub would seem most inadequate; but from the point of view of all-over skin condition I would suggest alternating tub and shower as a means of keeping crisp and refreshed.

PUMICE IS A FINE BATH AID

After a long soak in a warm tub rub away gently at calluses and cuticles with a pumice stone. It gradually removes layers of softened skin from corns that could harden and become annoying. Pumice used at tub times, little by little, can velvetize and smooth the hardening, roughening places on the feet. If they're cared for in this gentle manner, you'll find your feet serving you well without having to run to the podiatrist.

THE ART OF "KNEADING"

While bathing, knead away with the palm of your hand and fingertips at any excess flesh on the midriff, the flabby deposits on the buttocks, and by all means massage the flesh on your thighs between your fingers. Press and release, press and release, from ankle to hip bone. Rub each knee with both hands, up, and around . . . up, and around. It's so easy to massage like this under water. It may not thin you but, it makes tired legs feel like new and tightens and improves muscle tone.

TUB EXERCISE

The tub is an excellent place to exercise. In your morning warm water bath do some limbering, stretching; run through the hand and foot exercises, and even do your facial exercises. Water seems to make them easier, and if you are at all tense it will definitely help to untie the knots inside you.

BATHE INSIDE AND OUT

Many executives have learned the wisdom of keeping a carafe of water on the desk. Seeing it in front of them, they remember to drink occasionally. The skin, like the entire body, needs and craves water. Drink a glass of water before and after your bath. You will be getting in two more of those six glasses of water a day you need to rid the system of toxic substances, acids, and waste. Your kidneys will respond gratefully and so will your skin. But drink *between* meals, not with your meals.

Fresh as a Daisy and Free from Anxiety

When we come down to essentials, personal daintiness is based on meticulous cleanliness, which means not only frequent bathing but the regular use of a suitable deodorant or anti-perspirant to combat the after effects of perspiration.

Perspiration, a normal healthy excretion, is composed

of two main constituents: a watery free-flowing secretion of the eccrine glands and a thicker secretion of the apocrine glands. Eccrine glands are located almost everywhere on the body; the apocrine glands are found under the arm and at the groin. Offensive odors are caused by bacterial attack and decomposition of perspiration from the apocrine glands. Thus a good deodorant must not only check perspiration, it must also suppress odor by attacking its cause.

ANTI-PERSPIRANTS AND DEODORANTS

Anti-perspirants check perspiration and help to keep your underarms dry. They come in soft creams, some very neutral and some fragranced. They are pleasant and easy to use. That is why it has always been a puzzle to me why any sensible woman would risk being offensive or ruining her prettiest clothes with perspiration stains. For even when it is odorless, perspiration leaves rings on clothing that often will not vanish either with washing or dry cleaning.

Most anti-perspirants also deodorize, at least in the areas where they are used most—under the arms. Not every deodorant is also an anti-perspirant.

It is wise to remember *not* to apply anti-perspirants on the day you remove hair either by depilation or shaving. The skin in the armpit may be a little sensitive and become sore or erupt in a tiny rash. Let twenty-four hours elapse between depilation and applying any anti-perspirant.

I personally favor the combination deodorant and anti-perspirant. It seems to me more sensible to do two jobs in one, if you can. And now there are special anti-perspirant formulas containing antibiotics designed especially for those who require a more complete odor control.

The first spray anti-perspirants were neutral or non-scented. Recently, pleasantly perfumed spray deodorizer–anti-perspirants have been created and are especially welcomed by women who live in hot climates. The delicately scented deodorant accents the perfume you choose to wear.

Perfumed spray deodorant–anti-perspirants can also be used on the small of the back, or between the shoulders, where many women perspire freely, staining the backs of their dresses.

Palms of Hands and Anti-Perspirants

Even if it could be done it would be most unwise to stop all perspiration, yet there are times when nervousness or climate can cause the palms of the hands to become unpleasantly clammy and damp. An occasional quick spray with a deodorant–anti-perspirant can temporarily do away with this annoyance, or at least reduce it to the point of sparing you embarrassment.

DEPILATORIES AND THE HAIR ON YOUR BODY

It's natural for the skin to be covered with a fine down like a peach. Only if such hair is unnaturally dark and obvious should it be treated as superfluous hair. In some parts of the world this little extra hair is still considered a beauty-plus.

There is a myth that once you tamper with such body hair it comes back stronger and darker, or that once a strong growth is established nothing will clear it permanently, and that any electrical treatment scars the skin. These superstitions are just that—superstitions. They are not true. But it is essential to seek expert advice before deciding what should be done about superfluous hair.

Some women bleach the hair on upper lips, arms, and legs.

Others use one cream depilatory for facial hair, another for arms and legs. Such depilatories melt away hair, leaving the skin smooth and satiny. Other methods are waxing or electrolysis, both of which should be done by a professional.

If you have a really heavy growth on the face, electrolysis may be helpful.

In other times (and I can remember them well) there was some excuse for a cloud of black hair under a sheer stocking or for straggling hairs under a feminine chin. But thanks to modern science, special preparations, and skilled hands, no one has to live with this problem any longer.

Perfumes

Frequently, when I'm writing or talking about beauty, I have delved into the past. I am fascinated by the make-up techniques of the ancient Egyptians, the treatments used by the ladies of the court of Louis XIV, hair styles through the ages. But now I want to speak of perfume as if it existed only in a world of the future—your future.

The question most often asked me is, "How do I choose a perfume?" My answer is a simple one. Try one. If you respond to it, if you take pleasure in the fragrance, you will enjoy wearing it. It must first and foremost please *you*. It must express your taste and reveal your essential femininity. You may not know the reason you gravitate to a particular fragrance, but don't let externals, or even your dearest friends, influence your judgment. Choose the scent you love on *your* skin.

When selecting your fragrance, place a drop on your wrist or the inner curve on your elbow. You can then judge the scent itself—its holding power, how it reacts on your skin and your reaction to it. Perfume is a personal matter. It reflects the "climate" of your skin, its chemistry, its special warmth. On your skin a so-called ordinary perfume can have a heavenly fragrance, while a more expensive one may fade without a hint of the magic which makes perfume so enchanting.

Take your time when testing a new perfume. Never try more than one or two fragrances at one "testing." Put a few drops on each arm and see how it holds up during the day. Do you like it *more* or *less* each time you smell it?

Continue this process for a few weeks until you are accustomed to the fragrances that initially attracted you. Then settle on the perfume of your choice.

When you've used this one fragrance for a month and you are sure it's your favorite, you will be ready to expand your fragrance horizon. Gradually you will be able to acquire the related specialties that will bring out and intensify the bouquet of your special perfume—toilet water, spray cologne, bath powder, bath oil, soap. This amplification of fragrance was unknown in earlier days. It has come about only in our time, a sophisticated, delightful notion.

I would suggest that the choice of your first perfume should be one that is pleasing for both day and evening. Live with this one fragrance for a time before you reach for another.

And now, how to use perfume.

It is not enough to dab perfume behind the ears or to use it a drop at a time on a handkerchief. Fragrance should be used liberally for it to be recognized as a part of you—as a bath oil in your warm tub or smoothed on arms and shoulders after you shower, as a cologne sprayed from top to toe, as a dusting powder. The perfume itself —the pure, expensive essence—is then the last, wonderful "note" you dab or spray on lightly at the points where your pulse beat can be felt. The heat of your body will make it linger tantalizingly.

Sachets of your favorite fragrance are marvelous tucked into cupboards and drawers, since they will leave a lingering and delicate scent clinging to clothes, lingerie, linen, and all of your personal accessories.

If you find perfume essence is too costly, lavish yourself with eau de toilette which you can use extravagantly on body, hands, neck, and spray lightly over the hair. (Do this carefully because perfumes contain ingredients that can cause discoloration of tinted hair.)

Perfume is meant to follow you wherever you go. Use it at all times. Enjoy it in its subtle variations. Bathe with it, experiment with it, scent your clothes with it. But don't hoard bottles of scent. Once opened, they will evaporate and often lose their magic.

Your Beauty Schedule

Some women clean house from attic to cellar in a feverish onslaught of activity and then for months never dust a table. Day by day the house grows drearier, less attractive, until once more they are seized with a fury of cleaning.

Many people care for themselves in the same way.

That's why I like to remind women yearning for the look of polished perfection that maintaining a beauty schedule is an absolute must.

Set up your schedule based on the suggested one which follows, making your own variations and dovetailing it neatly with your other activities.

Good-Grooming Check List
Daily

Exercise
Morning Bath
    Deodorant—anti-perspirant
    Body-smooth lotion
    Dusting powder
    Cologne
Brushing of Teeth
Mouthwash
Morning Face Treatment
    Cleansing
    Astringent or freshener
    Moisturizer
Morning Make-up
Dressing
Hair Brushing
Hair Styling
Midday Make-up Freshening
Personal Laundry
    Lingerie, gloves, etc.
Night Face Treatment
Brushing of Teeth
    Dental floss

Weekly

Hair Conditioning
    Shampoo, set
Manicure
Pedicure
Depilation
Masque
Eyebrow Arch
    (Clean-up)
Wardrobe Checkup

Before a Glamorous Evening

Manipulate scalp, set hair, use hair spray lightly.

Tub bath with bath oil, apply cleansing cream, relax with
    pads on eyes.

After bath, apply body-smooth lotion, dusting powder,
    cologne, perfume to pulse spots.

Apply evening make-up.

10 Beauty Potpourri

Forget-me-nots for Memory

As I reread these pages, I realize how much more I could have said. To do full justice to the beauty knowledge available today I could write at least three books. For instance, I've skipped over the field of fashion: silhouette, line, and color. It has always enthralled me—like a fascinating serial story that never comes to an end. But fashion is superbly presented by skilled reporters for magazines and newspapers. They write timely and colorful stories about designers, clothes, and trends. Make a point of studying these fashion reports and being aware of what is new. It will help you choose the fashions best suited to your taste, your figure, the life you lead.

I could say much more about eyes. Not eye make-up (we covered that), but eye protection. It is so important to guard your eyes! They are priceless treasures. Never let a year pass without a checkup. Be glad for contact lenses and for glasses so beautifully and imaginatively designed that they attract rather than detract

Even if you don't need glasses for reading, invest in a pair of good sun glasses to protect your eyes and the delicate skin around them from the elements—the sun, particularly, and the glare. Glasses for the short- or long-sighted are no longer a one-pair-will-do utility. They can be keyed to formal and informal occasions. The color and shape of the frames are important. Hold the frame against your face as a test. Does it harmonize with the color of your hair and brows? Does the shape flatter your features?

What about the right eye make-up with glasses? Mascara should be applied lightly. (Avoid eye-shadow unless you wear contact lenses.) A clear eye-liner drawn across the upper lid, close to the lashes and out to the corner of the eye, gives emphasis to the eyes. If your lashes are long and thick, have the optometrist adjust the shape of the lenses so your lashes won't brush against them.

Legs—I could have included a few more paragraphs about legs. I do feel that the choice of the proper hosiery is important. Even though current fashion dictates bulky-knit and colored stockings, I will always believe that pretty legs look so much prettier in sheer, pale nylons. Don't let fashion guide you in spite of your better judgment.

A Salon Course—again, I could say a lot more. I believe any woman can benefit greatly from such a program of interrelated activities. Often it includes a diet for slimming, or for energy, with exercises planned to reproportion your figure where it's most needed. There is a certain amount of time devoted to the care of the skin and hair. And while you're about it, you'll have the opportunity to refresh your feeling for fashion, to find a new "look" that will make you feel bright and gay and younger than you have in years.

You can accomplish many of these objectives with a home beauty course. The only elements lacking are an outside monitor—or teacher—and a place to report. It's so much easier to cheat yourself than to cheat an instructor who says, "Well, madam, you weighed one hundred and forty-five pounds last week and you weigh one hundred and forty-five pounds this week. According to our findings, you should have lost about three pounds."

Then she looks at you quizzically, says nothing, but *she* knows all about those night raids on the icebox.

Backbone and determination are needed to carry out your own home beauty course. It may not be easy, but the results are wonderful. A few weeks of proper eating, limbering exercises, and concentration on improving your skin, hair and wardrobe can bring out a more radiant you than anyone would have suspected.

The Smile of Beauty

Have you ever considered the role a good dentist can play in your beauty thinking? Your new lipstick shade will look ever so much more attractive if your smile is white and sparkling. A periodic cleaning and scaling by your dentist should be as much a habit as your annual physical checkup. (Make a note of it on your calendar so you won't forget.)

There is no need to accept unattractive teeth as irremediable. The modern dentist can straighten teeth at almost any age. By correcting a tooth that juts forward and evening off those extra-long front teeth, he can practically alter the shape of your face. It may take patience and a little discomfort to make a mouth over, but it's worth it. Women often overlook this aspect of beauty because they've never thought of a dentist as someone they can seek out for cosmetic help. He is not merely the man who fixes teeth when they hurt—he is the man who can give you a lovelier smile.

The Art of Walking Gracefully

A beautiful walk is accomplished by those who do the most walking and carry the heaviest loads. In almost any country where the automobile is a comparative luxury you can see women walk with superlative grace. I have seen it in a hill town in Spain where the women carried water from the well, the clay jar riding smoothly on their heads—in Mexico where Indian women carry a child on their backs—in the Far East where small and delicately proportioned women walk with a regal air. They seem to know by instinct the art of balance which is part of any beautiful, gliding walk. There is no swinging of the weight from side to side. The feet placed deliberately, facing straight ahead to maintain smoothness and balance.

I know of no better way to acquire a beautiful walk than the time-tested one of walking with a book on one's head. Walk quickly, body held upright, without letting the book fall to the ground. Add a second book, then a third, and when you can carry up to four or five books on your head, you will begin to have a feeling about moving smoothly that will set you apart as a woman of elegance and magnificent carriage.

It's much harder to develop a beautiful walk in high heels. Start practicing without shoes . . . then in flats . . . then wearing medium heels, and *finally* high heels. Observe every woman you know, to find out not only how to move but how *not* to. Valuable lessons can be learned from bad examples as well as good ones.

Spice for Wit and Wonder

The lengths to which some women will go in pursuit of elegance is, at times, incomprehensible. It has often added a touch of humor to an otherwise serious business. I recall a woman who arrived at my New York salon when it opened one Monday morning. She was carrying a parcel, which she opened carefully, revealing a fine porcelain plate banded in a rich shade of dubonnet. "Now," she said to the make-up consultant, "I want you to find me a lipstick and nail varnish that matches this plate border exactly! I'm giving a dinner party tonight and I must look as if I 'belong' to the table." We found them for her!

Then there was the lady who came into the hair-coloring salon with a mink coat over her arm. "Match it!" she stated. "To my hair, I mean. I intend to be coordinated." We coordinated her hair to match her mink!

And there was an ambassador's wife (from one of our neighboring Latin American countries) who came with a spray of eighteen pink orchids, requesting, "My hair must be as beautiful as a jungle . . . silver and gold laced with these orchids . . ." We did our best!

These are only a few of the odd requests we have received and carried out to the satisfaction of our clients. They may call for a little ingenuity, but that is a vital part of the beauty industry.

Rosemary for Remembrance

I often find it hard to believe that my own business, which has introduced more than a thousand beauty preparations, started with a single face cream used every night by my mother. As a "retiring ritual" my mother never failed to apply this cream to her skin—and later to mine and my seven sisters'. Even today when I meet parents who are concerned about what they are doing for their youngsters I think of that little pot of cream and how strongly it impressed me because my mother truly believed in what it could do for her skin. Certainly she wanted to pass on other, greater gifts to her daughters than just good skin care. But what parent can tell when some such fragmentary gift of knowledge or wisdom will enrich her children's lives? Or how a small seed of information passed from one generation to another may generate a new science, a new industry—a seed which neither the giver nor the receiver can truly evaluate at the time. What my mother gave me with her love and affection has grown into something she could never have imagined. My first cream was the cornerstone of my life. . . . Isn't this one of the keys of life? To share with affection and let the rest take care of itself with time!

When I was a young woman I often felt a sense of resentment toward my business. It left me so little time for my husband and for my children.

During those first years I was like a child who had found a magic mill. It fascinated me. I worked unceasingly to develop new products and to expand my services in new directions. In later years I could appreciate how my business kept me occupied and close to young people everywhere in the world. In old age I have no regrets because I now realize that I don't just sell beauty preparations. I believe that my long lifetime of working and striving has answered a need and fulfilled an important function in helping women to find their rightful heritage of beauty. As is often the case, we start out to find success and while doing so we find humanity. Or should I say, humanity finds us!

LEARN WHAT YOGA CAN DO FOR YOU

☐ **YOGA FOR BEAUTY AND HEALTH**
by Eugene Rawls and Eve Diskin

Become more alive, more confident, serene and attractive—burst with energy and ambition—as you follow the proved teachings of Eugene Rawls and Eve Diskin, two of America's most famous and expert Yoga instructors.
(55-740, 95¢)

☐ **THE YOGA COOKBOOK** by Edna Thompson

Hundreds of tempting vegetarian recipes have been selected to provide the specific Yoga foods necessary to synchronize a healthy body with a serene mind.
(64-012, 75¢)

☐ **RENEW YOUR LIFE THROUGH YOGA** by Indra Devi

Discover the safe, sane, proven way to improve your mental and physical health. Practice the Indra Devi method for relaxation through rhythmic breathing.
(65-128, 95¢)

☐ **YOGA FOR TODAY**
by Clara Spring and Madeleine Goss

Easy-to-understand chapters on mind and meditation; Yoga and sex; relaxation and sleep; postures for special breathing and body-cleansing procedures. (65-159, 95¢)

☐ **EXECUTIVE YOGA** by Archie J. Bahm

Executive Yoga contains practical, authentic Yoga exercises for today's busy business and professional person that will help you get more out of the job—*without* the job taking more out of you! (66-307, $1.25)

MORE BOOKS FOR GOOD HEALTH AND ENERGY

☐ **MARTINIS & WHIPPED CREAM:** *The New Carbo-Cal Way To Lose Weight and Stay Slim*
by Sidney Petrie in association with Robert B. Stone

The only calories you count are carbohydrates. Enjoy fried foods, appetizers, gravies, sauces, dressings, ice cream, and even martinis and whipped cream. Never feel hungry or guilty again. (65-017, 95¢)

☐ **GET YOUR SHAPE IN SHAPE**
by Fran Hair and Rita Chazen

Look and feel like a new woman. Come alive—look more attractive, in only 30 minutes a day with this new, effective exercise plan! (64-208, 75¢)

INVALUABLE REFERENCE BOOKS
YOU WILL WANT TO OWN!

☐ **HOUSE PLANTS FOR EVERY WINDOW**
by Dorothy H. Jenkins and Helen Van Pelt Wilson

How to grow and care for over 300 plants. "The most popular book on house plants ever written."
—*The Charlotte News* (53-528, 60¢)

☐ **PAPERBACK LIBRARY CROSSWORD PUZZLE BOOK #1** compiled by The Chicago Tribune-New York News Syndicate

Over 50 challenging, medium-to-hard puzzles from THE CHICAGO TRIBUNE. So sharpen your pencil—and your wits—and begin! (52-765, 50¢)

☐ **SEW SIMPLY, SEW RIGHT**
by Mini Rhea and Frances S. Leighton

Sew Simply, Sew Right is an easy-to-follow guide to making your own clothes, from the first stitch to the finishing touches which give your garment that professional look. (64-285, 75¢)

☐ **HOW TO AVOID INSOMNIA**
by Gay Gaer Luce and Dr. Julius Segal

The latest scientific findings about why you can't sleep—and what you can do about it; sleep research; sleep myths; dreams and nightmares; sex and sleep; drugs and sleep; effective sleep techniques without drugs. (66-533, $1.25)

☐ **GETTING THE MOST FOR YOUR MONEY**
by Anthony Scaduto

This book can save you thousands of dollars by showing you how to buy, where to buy, and when to buy. (65-607, 95¢)

☐ **300 WAYS TO MOONLIGHT** by Jerry LeBlanc

Three hundred ways to make money in your spare-time—business ideas, things to make and sell, part-time jobs. There's something here for everyone! (64-274, 75¢)

☐ **THE SINGLE GIRL'S GUIDE TO EUROPE**
by Andrea Kenis

How to handle money, manners, museums and *men*—and plan the best vacation of your life. (65-561, 95¢)

DELICIOUS COOKBOOKS
FROM PAPERBACK LIBRARY

☐ **COOKING FOR TWO** by Ted and Jean Kaufman
Over 300 gourmet recipes for exotic, savory dishes designed just for two. (54-671, 75¢)

☐ **GRANDMOTHER'S COUNTRY COOKBOOK**
by Ted and Jean Kaufman
Nearly 500 authentic, unusual recipes for delicious dishes from rural American kitchens. (55-381, 95¢)

☐ **THE COMPLETE BOOK OF HOME FREEZING**
by Hazel Meyer
"Every homemaker who owns or plans to buy a home freezer should also own this practical, readable handbook."—*Parents' Magazine* (55-476, 95¢)

☐ **POPPY CANNON'S BRIDE'S COOKBOOK**
by Poppy Cannon
The well-known cook gives simple, easy-to-follow instructions for preparing the most basic foods—like brewing perfect coffee, scrambling eggs or broiling a steak—as well as recipes for gourmet dishes even the most experienced chef will envy. (65-339, 95¢)

☐ **JAMES BEARD'S FISH COOKERY**
"Just about all the information you'll ever need to know about choosing and cooking fish is contained in this cookbook."—*The Houston Post* (55-432, 95¢)

☐ **THE COMPLETE ROUND THE WORLD HORS D'OEUVRES BOOK** by Myra Waldo
There's nothing like different hors d'oeuvres to start a meal right—or make a party bright. You'll find these truly original recipes are "on target for sophisticated jet-age tastes."—*Philadelphia Inquirer* (53-537, 60¢)

☐ **GERMAN COOKING** by Elizabeth Schuler
Germany's most famous, most popular cookbook shows you how to prepare hearty, mouth-watering dishes from *apfelstrudel* to *zweibelfleisch*. (54-772, 75¢)

☐ **FRENCH COOKING FOR AMERICANS** by Louis Diat
Over 600 gourmet recipes specially adapted for American kitchens. "Provides fine guidance for those . . . who don't know their possibilities."—*The New York Times* (54-416, 75¢)